This book belongs to:

Justin Gear.

IN (- CV.

Disney Boys' Big Book of Fun

CREDITS
Pages 10–11 | "THE COMIC HIJINKS OF NORM AND DOOF"
Writer: Scott Peterson; Pencils/Inks/Colors/Letters: John Green
Based on the series created by Dan Povenmire & Jeff "Swampy" Marsh ©2011 Disney Enterprises, Inc.
Pages 42–45 | TOOLS OF THE TRADE
Text: Alessandro Sisti; Pencils: Valentino Forlini; Ink: Michela Frare; Colors: Kawaii Creative Studio
Page 48 | DEEDS, NOT WORDS!
Text: Alessandro Sisti; Pencils: Valentino Forlini; Ink: Michela Frare; Colors: Kawaii Creative Studio
Pages 62–63 | DOOFENSHMIRTZ JINGLES INCORPORATED
By Deb Barnes
Pages 68–71 | NEW FRIENDS
Text: Alessandro Sisti; Layout: Luca Usai; Ink: Michela Frare; Colors: Lucio De Giuseppe
Pages 72–75 | TOP SECRET
By Deb Barnes
Pages 76–79 | JAM-MATER ROCKS OUT
Text: Niccolò De Moiana; Pencils: Valentino Forlini; Ink: Michela Frare; Colors: Kawaii Creative Studio
Page 80 | "SECRETS FROM THE OWCA: THE ORGANIZATION WITHOUT A COOL ACRONYM"
Text: Scott Peterson; Pencils: John Green; Inks: Mike DeCarlo; Colors: Emily Kanalz; Letters: Michael Stewart
Based on the series created by Dan Povenmire & Jeff "Swampy" Marsh
©2010 Disney Enterprises, Inc.
Page 81 | "AND NOW . . . FERB'S WORDS OF WISDOM"
Text: Scott Peterson; Pencils: John Green; Inks: Mike DeCarlo; Colors: Emily Kanalz; Letters: Michael Stewart;
Based on the series created by Dan Povenmire & Jeff "Swampy" Marsh
©2010 Disney Enterprises, Inc.
Page 95 | NAPKIN DOG
Script: Tea Orsi; Layout & ink: Valentino Forlini; Colour: Lucio De Giuseppe
Page 97 | SUPER SECRET HIDE-AND-SEEK
Text: Alessandro Ferrari; Pencil: Valentino Forlini; Ink: Michela Frare; Colors: Kawaii Creative Studio
Pages 98–99 | PHASCINATING PHACTS
By Suzanne Robertson
Page 100 | FAMILY SIZE
Text: Frank Strom; Pencils: Al Bigley; Inks: Matt Maley; Letters: Michael Stewart; Colors: Garry Black
©2012 Disney/Pixar
Page 101 | A WORK OF ART
Text: Frank Strom; Pencils: Al Bigley; Inks: Matt Maley; Letters: Michael Stewart; Colors: Garry Black
©2012 Disney/Pixar
Pages 102–105 | "THE FEAR PARTY"
Text: Alessandro Ferrari; Layouts: Emilio Urbano; Pencils: Manuela Razzi; Paints: Charles Pickens; Letterer: Patrick Brosseau
Pages 106–111 | PLUTO'S SURPRISE PACKAGE
Text: di Alberto Savini; Art: Enrico Faccini
Page 112 | A DIFFERENT KIND OF RACE!
Text: Alessandro Sisti; Layout and pencils: Valentino Forlini; Ink: Michela Frare; Colors: Kawaii Creative Studio
Page 113 | LAUNDRY DAY
Text: Alessandro Sisti; Layout and pencils: Valentino Forlini; Ink: Michela Frare; Colors: Kawaii Creative Studio
Page 123 | WORDS IN THE DARK
Text: Tea Orsi; Layout: Valentino Forlini; Ink: Valentino Forlini; Colors: Lucio De Giuseppe
Page 129 | YEE OF LITTLE FAITH
Text: Niccolò De Moiana; Pencils and ink: Michela Frare; Color: Kawaii Creative Studio
Page 130–131 | "THE GLOVE CHALLENGE"
Text: Alessandro Ferrari; Layouts: Emilio Urbano; Pencils: Manuela Razzi; Paints: Mara Damiani; Letterer: Patrick Brosseau
Pages 132–135 | A DIRTY TRICK
Text: Gabriele Panini; Pencils: Valentino Forlini; Ink: Michela Frare; Colors: Kawaii Creative Studio
Pages 136–143 | CRASH COURSE
Text: Frank Strom; Pencils: Al Bigley; Inks: Matt Maley; Letters: Michael Stewart; Colors: Garry Black
©2012 Disney/Pixar
Page 144 | WHO LAUGHS FIRST?
Text: Tea Orsi, Pencils & ink: Valentino Forlini, Colors: Angela Capolupo
Pages 160–163 | PIT STOP
Text: Niccolò De Moiana; Pencils: Valentino Forlini; Ink: Michela Frare; Colors: Kawaii Creative Studio
Pages 164–167 | SPACE COMEDY
Text: Alessandro Ferrari; Layout & ink: Valentino Forlini; Colors: Mara Damiani & Angela Capolupo
Page 168 | LASSO BOOMERANG
Text: Alessandro Sisti; Layout & ink: Luca Usai; Colors: Mara Damiani & Lucio De Giuseppe

This edition published by Parragon Books Ltd in 2014
and distributed by

Parragon Inc.
440 Park Avenue South, 13th Floor
New York, NY 10016
www.parragon.com

ISBN 978-1-4723-4149-5

Printed in China

Disney

Boys' Big Book of Fun

SCAREONOMICS

I'M SCARY, YOU'RE SCARY

THE POWER OF SCREAMS

COMPLETE MONSTER
ENCYCLOPEDIA

Bath · New York · Cologne · Melbourne · Delhi
Hong Kong · Shenzhen · Singapore · Amsterdam

HELLO
FRANCESCO BERNOULLI
THE ITALIAN RACER

BUONA SERA!

ITALY

NAME: FRANCESCO BERNOULLI

DETAILS: FORMULA RACING CHAMPION

PERSONAL FEATURES: SPEED AND SELF-CONFIDENCE

EQUIPMENT: VISIBLE TIRES, SLEEK BODY

SKILL: SPEED!

SPOILER

FRONT AND REAR SPOILERS ADD STABILITY AND KEEP RACERS FROM TIPPING OVER AT HIGH SPEEDS.

INTAKE SYSTEM

IT TAKES IN AIR TO COOL THE ENGINE AND BRAKES, AND PROVIDES ADDITIONAL SPEED.

REAR SPOILER

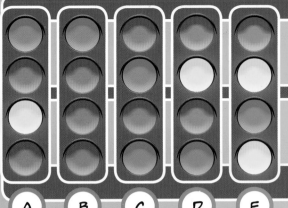

A   B   C   D   E

READY, SET ... GO!

WHICH OF THESE TRAFFIC LIGHTS SHOWS THE SAME SEQUENCE AS THE ONE BELOW?

THE RIGHT SEQUENCE

PASTA POTENZA

ROTELLI TIRES

TIRES

DIFFERENT TYPES ARE USED FOR DRY AND WET ROAD SURFACES.

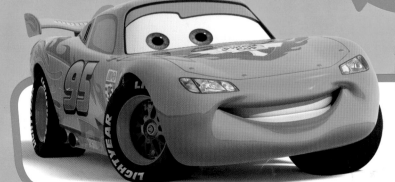

HIS MAIN RACING OPPONENT

LIGHTNING AND FRANCESCO RACE EACH OTHER IN THE WORLD GRAND PRIX.

7

Answer on page 171

WHAT KIND OF MONSTER ARE YOU?

So you want to work at Monsters, Inc., but you aren't sure exactly where you'll fit in? Take this test and find out!

09132

74301

1

You're on the Scare Floor at Monsters, Inc., and you notice that a door has been left open. You would most likely:

- ■ a. Go tell your boss.
- ■ b. Slam the door shut and call the Child Detection Agency (CDA).
- ■ c. Walk through the door to see if there's a child around to scare.
- ■ d. Close the door and search the entire building to see if a child has escaped.

2

You notice that a monster has just come out of a scare door with a child's sock on his back. You would most likely:

- ■ a. Scream for the CDA.
- ■ b. Grab a notebook and write down the date and time.
- ■ c. Let the CDA take care of it while you scare another child.
- ■ d. Grab a pair of tongs and tackle the monster to get the sock off his back.

8

3

You notice that another monster has brought food onto the Scare Floor. You would most likely:

- ■ a. Go over and quietly remind the monster that food is not allowed on the Scare Floor.
- ■ b. Report the monster to his boss immediately.
- ■ c. Keep scaring kids and collecting screams.
- ■ d. Yell "FOOD ON THE SCARE FLOOR!" and tackle the monster to the ground.

4

On your days off, you would most likely:

- ■ a. Go to the movies.
- ■ b. Go to the office to work—there are papers to be filed!
- ■ c. Read *Innovations in Scaring*.
- ■ d. Go shopping for tongs.

5

Which of the movies listed below would you most like to see?

- ■ a. *A Far, Far Galaxy: Part 19.*
- ■ b. *Filing Cabinets Are Your Friends.*
- ■ c. *The Greatest Scarer on Earth.*
- ■ d. *The Thing That Escaped Through the Closet Door.*

6

Your friends would most likely describe you as:

- ■ a. Fun.
- ■ b. A neat freak.
- ■ c. Scary.
- ■ d. Bossy.

SCREAM-O-METER

3080051

YOUR RESULTS

Mostly "a"

You know how to follow rules but you don't need to be in the spotlight. You're lighthearted and fun. You'd be terrific as a Monsters, Inc. Scare Assistant or Receptionist, or at any job where it's important to keep those around you relaxed and happy.

Mostly "b"

You're more concerned with rules than you are with people. Provided you aren't mean, too, you would make excellent management material.

Mostly "c"

You don't think about anything other than scaring kids— and we need as many Scarers as we can get. If you're interested in a monstrously fun career, sign up as a Scarer today!

Mostly "d"

You're bold and bossy and like a challenge. You would make an excellent CDA agent!

"THE COMIC HIJINKS OF NORM AND DOOF"

THE END

11

MEET THE

CHECK OUT THE CHARACTERS WHO LIVE IN

WRECK-IT RALPH

GAME:
Fix-It Felix, Jr.
AFFILIATION:
Bad Guy who wants to be the Good Guy

POWERS:
Able to destroy anything
NOTABLE CHARACTERISTICS:
Always wears overalls over one shoulder; 9 feet tall; weighs 643 pounds; uses gigantic fists to "wreck" things
STRENGTHS:
Super strong, determined
WEAKNESSES:
A bit klutzy; some anger issues

> I'M GONNA WRECK IT!

FIX-IT FELIX, JR.

GAME:
Fix-It Felix, Jr.
AFFILIATION:
Good Guy

POWERS:
Able to fix anything—especially whatever Ralph wrecks
NOTABLE CHARACTERISTICS:
Cheerful, can-do attitude; wields magic hammer that can fix anything that is broken or doesn't work
STRENGTHS:
Dependable, lightning-quick reflexes; super nice to everyone
WEAKNESSES:
Nice to the point of being naïve; gets a distracting "honey glow" when near Sergeant Calhoun

CHARACTERS

WRECK–IT RALPH'S MOST POPULAR GAMES!

SERGEANT CALHOUN

GAME:
Hero's Duty
AFFILIATION:
Good Guy

POWERS:
Outstanding military leader and strategist, weapons expert
NOTABLE CHARACTERISTICS:
Tall, strong, tough as nails; keeps her troops in line; carries impressive weaponry; rides a cruiser (a cool hovering board)
STRENGTHS:
Smart, highly trained; dedicated to her mission
WEAKNESSES:
"Weakness" isn't in her vocabulary

VANELLOPE VON SCHWEETZ

GAME:
Sugar Rush
AFFILIATION:
Good Guy—er . . . Girl, actually

POWERS:
Nimble, quick, great climber; natural kart-racing talent
NOTABLE CHARACTERISTICS:
Sassy, determined 9-year-old; really wants to race again
STRENGTHS:
Persistent, resourceful, competitive
WEAKNESSES:
Sharp tongue and constant chatter can make her a bit annoying at times

KING CANDY

GAME:
Sugar Rush
AFFILIATION:
He says he's the Good Guy . . .

POWERS:
Rules the Sugar Rush game and orders other characters around; his kart can fire candies as weapons
NOTABLE CHARACTERISTICS:
Small, overly jolly; drives the game's most tricked-out racing kart; fond of tossing candy to crowds
STRENGTHS:
Cunning, skilled and competitive driver; can access game's inner workings
WEAKNESSES:
Controlling, power hungry

PROFILE
Peas-in-a-Pod & Aliens

These two green threesomes always stick together.

HEY YOU, PEA BRAIN!

When the Peas-in-a-Pod first meet Woody at Bonnie's house they think that he is not a real cowboy, because he has lost his cowboy hat.

FACTS
- The Peas-in-a-Pod is one of the toys owned by Bonnie. Their names are Peatey, Peatrice, and Peanelope.
- The Peas-in-a-Pod are six times bigger than a real pea.

OOOOOOOOOO!

The Aliens have a thing for "the CLAW", which is what saves Woody and the gang in Toy Story 3.

THE CLAW!!

FACTS

- The Aliens come from the restaurant Pizza Planet, where they escaped with the help of the CLAW.

- The Aliens are sort of adopted by Mr. and Mrs. Potato Head.

COLOR

LEGGED TOYS

It's time for Bonnie to clean her room.
Help her sort the toys in the two boxes by
counting the number of legs each one has.

MISSION ACCOMPLISHED!

COLOR WHEN FINISHED

4 LEGS   2 LEGS

TOY MATCH!

Woody, Jessie, and Buzz are each looking for their perfect match. Draw a line between each color picture and the correct black & white one.

MISSION ACCOMPLISHED!

COLOR
WHEN
FINISHED

Answers on page 171

17

SKY VIEW

LIGHTYEA[R]

1 BLIMP EYE

ONLY FIVE OF THE 10 CIRCLED PICTURES HAVE BEEN FILMED BY AL OFT IN THIS SCENE. WHICH ONES ARE THEY?

2 DRILL TEAM

COUNT THE CARS IN EACH LETTER, THEN ADD THEM UP BY COLOR.

BLUE CARS				
P	T	C		TOTAL
8	+ ...	+ ...	=	...

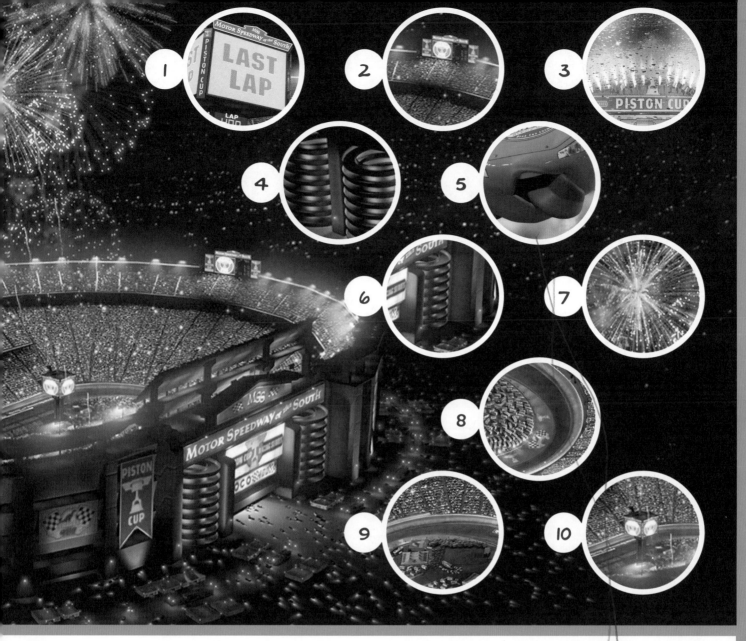

YELLOW CARS

I	O	U	TOTAL
... +	... +	... =	...

RED CARS

S	N	P	TOTAL
... +	... +	... =	...

Answers on page 171

FRIGHTENING FUN

S
W
I
O
K
W
Z
A

NAME DROPPING

What's Mike's last name?
Untangle the lines and find out!

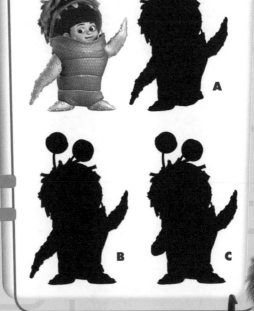

ALL FOR ONE

Three shadows are too many.
Which shadow matches Boo perfectly?

A   B   C

20

Answers on page 171

A-MAZE-ING
MONSTROPOLIS

Mike and Sulley have to get to Monsters, Inc. quick! Can you help them navigate the streets of Monstropolis so they won't be late for work?

Answer on page 171

ROLL CALL

Meet the Scarers of tomorrow at Monsters University!

Spends his Saturday nights studying. After all, finals are only a few months away!

MIKE WAZOWSKI

This straight-A scare student has wanted to be a Scarer all his life. He knows all the tricks, but can he be scary enough to use them?

DRAW MIKE HERE!

MIKE HAS A BIG EYE AND AN EVEN BIGGER HEART.

JAMES P. "SULLEY" SULLIVAN

He's the life of the party and would rather hang out at the fraternity house than study.

DRAW SULLEY HERE!

A NATURAL TALENT, SULLEY COMES FROM A FAMILY OF SUCCESSFUL SCARERS.

Confident and stubborn, Sulley has his share of doubts—and getting him to open up about them isn't easy!

LETTER GAME

Find the first letter in these toys' names on the yellow notepaper. Cross them out when you've used them.

Answers on page 171

SOCCER TWINS?

Only two of the players in the box are really identical. Circle them!

1

2

3

4

5

6

7

LUCKY KICK

There are seven differences between the two pictures of Gladstone Gander. Can you spot them?

Answers on page 171

THE BIG MATCH

Complete the puzzle by finding the missing piece from the five pictures below.

nswer on page 171

SPACE COLOR

Buzz Lightyear is off on a daring mission. Set the scene and color him in using the color-key guide.

DRAW IT!

CREATE A ROBOT VERSION OF YOURSELF JUST LIKE THE PHINEAS AND FERB ROBOTS! IMAGINE ALL THE EXTRA FUN [AND HELP] YOU CAN HAVE TO MAKE EACH DAY THE BEST EVER!

TAPE YOUR SCHOOL PICTURE IN THE CENTER BOX. THEN DRAW THE REST OF YOUR ROBOT-SELF AROUND IT. DON'T FORGET TO NAME YOUR ROBOT!

TAPE YOUR
SCHOOL PHOTO
HERE.

ROBOT NAME:

EXTREME CLOSE-UP

NAME THESE *PHINEAS AND FERB* LOCATIONS!

1

2

3

4

5

6

7

8

9

10

HIDE-AND-SEEK

Every good monster knows how to hide! Who's hiding on this page?
Use the color dots to fill in the picture below to find out!

Answer on page 171

DID YOU SEE THAT?

A good Scarer always pays attention to details!
Can you find the 10 differences between these pictures?

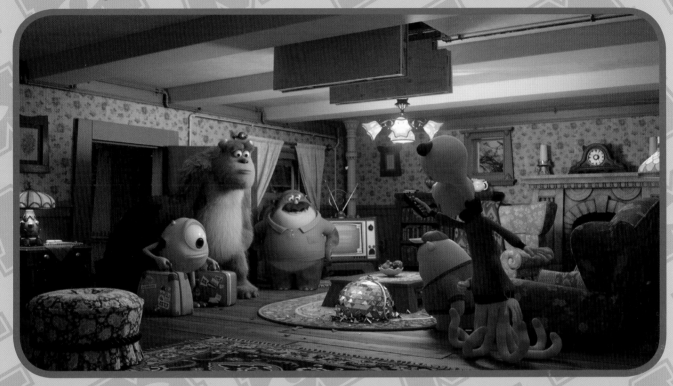

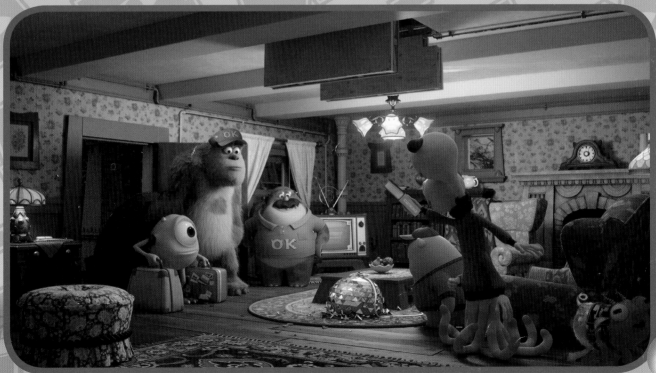

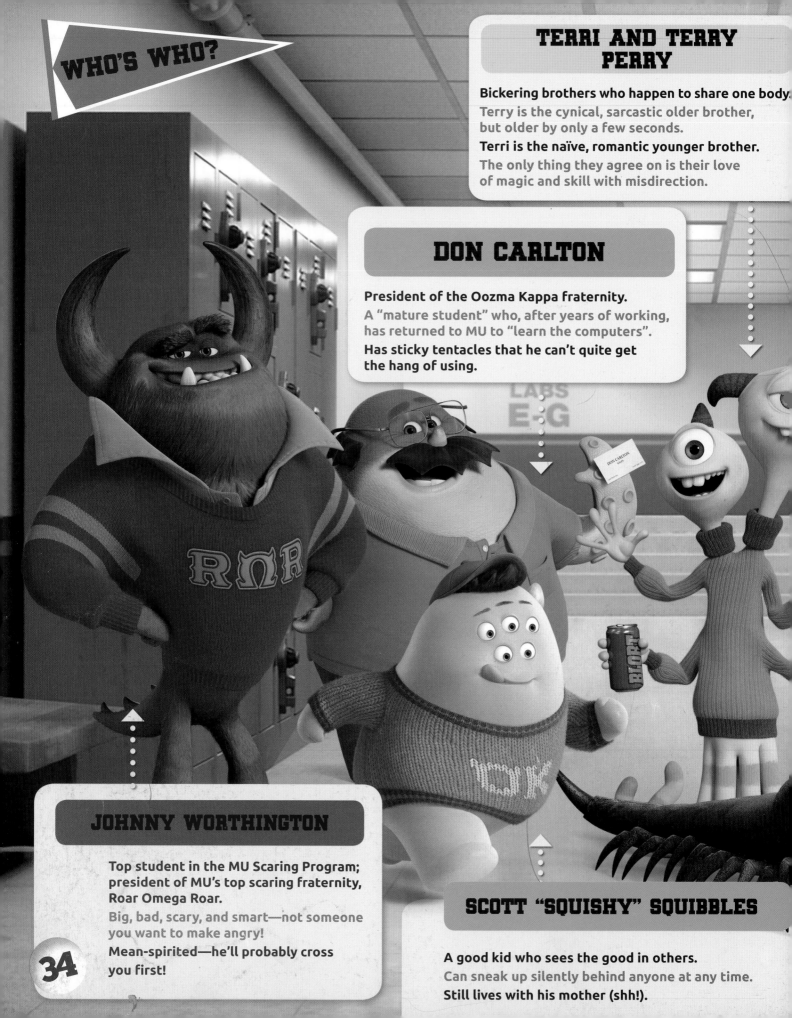

TERRI AND TERRY PERRY

Bickering brothers who happen to share one body.

Terry is the cynical, sarcastic older brother, but older by only a few seconds.

Terri is the naïve, romantic younger brother.

The only thing they agree on is their love of magic and skill with misdirection.

DON CARLTON

President of the Oozma Kappa fraternity.

A "mature student" who, after years of working, has returned to MU to "learn the computers".

Has sticky tentacles that he can't quite get the hang of using.

JOHNNY WORTHINGTON

Top student in the MU Scaring Program; president of MU's top scaring fraternity, Roar Omega Roar.

Big, bad, scary, and smart—not someone you want to make angry!

Mean-spirited—he'll probably cross you first!

34

SCOTT "SQUISHY" SQUIBBLES

A good kid who sees the good in others.

Can sneak up silently behind anyone at any time.

Still lives with his mother (shh!).

DEAN HARDSCRABBLE

Terrifying dean of the MU School of Scaring.

Record-breaking Scarer and creator of the Scare Games.

She is tough on her scare students, but she's never been wrong about their potential...yet.

RANDY BOGGS

Mike's roommate is sweet and a bit naïve.

Needs a confidence boost and will do almost anything to impress those he admires.

Has a natural camouflage ability that he thinks is lame, but it could come in handy.

ART

Weird, loud, and in touch with his inner feelings—though he doesn't seem to care too much about anyone else's.

Positive and up for anything...maybe too much!

May or may not have been in jail.

ARCHIE THE SCARE PIG

Mascot of MU's rival school, Fear Tech.

Stolen by Sulley to give to the Roar Omega Roars.

Watch out, he bites!

HOW TO SCARE LIKE A PRO!

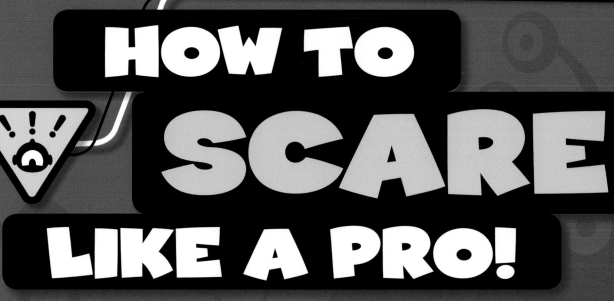

Want to become a top Scarer for Monsters, Inc.? Try out some of these scaring techniques straight from the pros. Remember, practice makes perfect!

OL' WATERNOOSE JUMP-AND-GROWL

One of the oldest and most reliable scaring tactics practiced at Monsters, Inc., the Ol' Waternoose Jump-and-Growl is most effective when done quickly. Before going through the closet, grip the door handle firmly. In one quick motion, throw the door open and leap into the child's room, emitting a low growl ending with a fierce snarl.

WARNING!

MOST EFFECTIVE WHEN DONE QUICKLY!

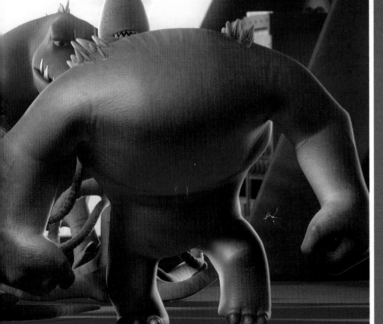

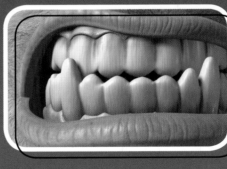

SULLIVAN ULTRA ROAR

The success of this technique depends mostly on volume and timing. Wait until your child has just fallen asleep. Then open the closet door and roar as loudly as possible. Guaranteed to scare the braces off any kid.

WARNING!

ACTUAL CONTACT WITH ANY CHILD IS STRICTLY PROHIBITED, BECAUSE CHILDREN ARE HIGHLY TOXIC!

BOGGS QUICK REVEAL

Pioneered by Randall Boggs, this technique is most easily performed by Scarers with chameleon-like properties. However, a non-chameleon Scarer can use this technique simply by silently sneaking up behind someone and waiting for him or her to turn around. Frighteningly effective!

THE POTATO HEADS & THE ALIENS

Mr. and Mrs. Potato Head are a perfect match, and what more do a happy couple need than three children? Even if the children are Aliens!

Mr. Potato Head saves the Aliens in the crazy car chase in Toy Story 2. And Mrs. Potato Head wants to adopt them!

MY SWEET POTATO!

MY HERO!

TOOLS OF THE TRADE

NOW HE'S GOT TO TOW THEM BACK TO THEIR PASTURE!

IT'LL TAKE HIM ALL DAY!

NEED A WHEEL, MATER?

THANKS, FINN! I'LL SHOW YOU HOW IT'S DONE!

MOO!

YOU HAVE TO LASSO 'EM . . .

. . . AND THEN GET THEM TO FOLLOW YOU! THEY'RE A LITTLE STUBBORN!

LOOKS EASY ENOUGH!

THIS CALLS FOR A TOW CABLE BUT YOU DON'T HAVE ONE!

The End

CAMPUS LIVING

Get to know the MU fraternities and sororities!

OK
OOZMA KAPPA

A supportive group of students who have been cut from the Scaring Program. Their skills may be lacking, but this odd bunch may have a surprise or two up their many sleeves.

JΘX
JAWS THETA CHI

Size matters to these monsters; they're all brawn and not so big on brains. They'll do whatever it takes to win ... even if they have to cheat.

ΣΣΚ
SLUGMA SLUGMA KAPPA

These athletic sorority sisters are always practicing for the Scare Games; they don't even go home for the holidays.

EXTREME CLOSE-UP!

Take a much closer look at these students! Can you figure out which house each belongs to?

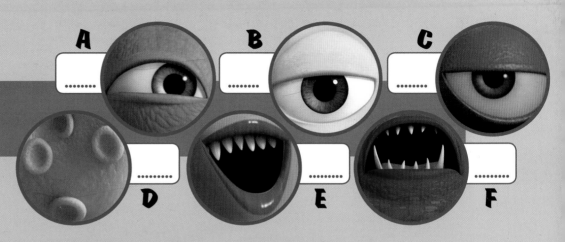

A ....

B ....

C ....

D ....

E ....

F ....

RΩR

ROAR OMEGA ROAR

MU's top scaring fraternity, with a frighteningly good winning streak in the Scare Games. Roar Omega Roar's elite members will stop at nothing to stay on top.

PNK

PYTHON NU KAPPA

Don't be fooled by their cheery smiles and cute pink outfits—these sorority sisters are clever, cold, and scheming.

HSS

ETA HISS HISS

Not much is known about these mysterious sisters, besides their goth wardrobe and fearsome demeanor.

nswers on page 171

DEEDS, NOT WORDS!

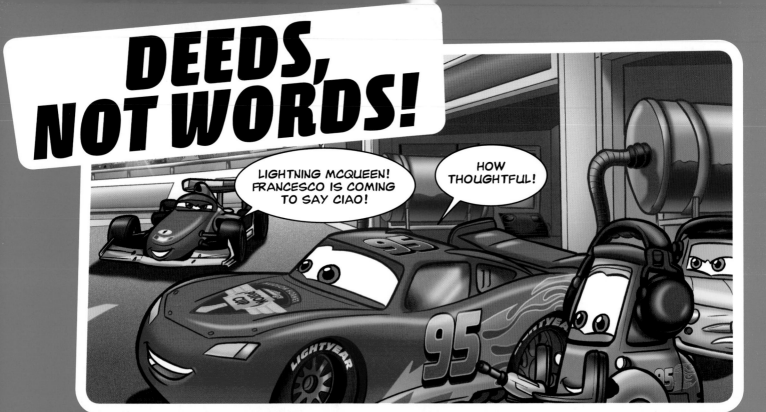

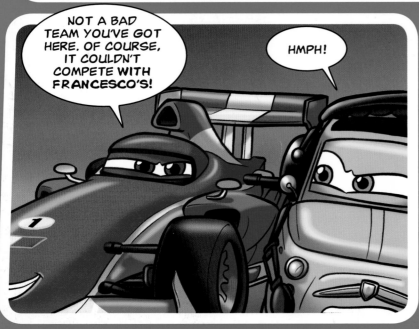

The End

OUT OF FOCUS

THE PHOTO IN THE WHITE FRAME IS OUT OF FOCUS. WHICH PICTURE—
A, B, OR C—IS THE CORRECT VERSION OF THE BLURRED PHOTO?

A

B

C

FIND THE DETAILS

THERE ARE MISSING PIECES IN THE PICTURE BELOW. FIND EACH ONE
AT THE BOTTOM AND WRITE THE CORRECT NUMBER UNDER IT.

1
2
3
4
5

A ... B ... C ... D ... E ...

Answers on page 171

49

SOCCER FIX

Complete the picture, choosing from the five pieces below. Watch out for the two that don't fit!

A GAME OF SHADOWS

Greedy Gus Goose cannot go without a snack, even when he is on the field! Which shadow belongs to Gus? Look carefully and find the only one that fits perfectly!

Answers on page 17

A REFLECTION OF GOLD

Scrooge McDuck and his reflection don't match perfectly! Spot the eight differences!

ORIGINAL T-SHIRT

Mickey must take to the field. What shirt should he wear? Help him find the only shirt that isn't part of a pair!

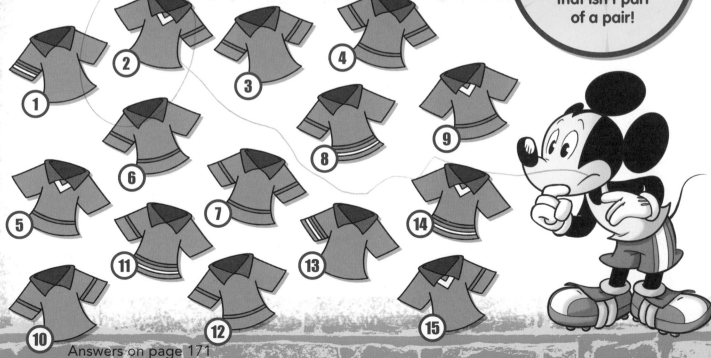

PUZZLE MINUTE

Here are some great puzzles for you to dig into. So grab your pen, and get to it!

1 SHADOW HUNT
Draw a line between each toy and its shadow.

4 COUNT ALL THE STARS
How many stars can you find on these two pages?

....

52

WHERE DO YOU BELONG?

Which fraternity or sorority would be your best fit at Monsters University? Take this quiz to find out!

START HERE!

YES

DO YOU LIKE TO EXERCISE IN YOUR SPARE TIME?

YES

NO

DO YOU THINK SUCCESS IS MORE IMPORTANT THAN FRIENDSHIP?

NO

DO YOU HAVE A WICKED SENSE OF HUMOR?

YES

NO

ROAR OMEGA ROAR

IS THE OLDEST FRATERNITY ON CAMPUS AND HAS WON THREE SCARE GAMES IN A ROW.

DO YOU THINK BRAWN IS MORE IMPORTANT THAN BRAINS?

YES

JOX
You love to stay in shape. But try not to ignore your classes!

NO

DO YOU THINK EVERYONE SHOULD HAVE AN EQUAL SAY IN YOUR GROUP ACTIVITIES?

NO

RΩR
You're driven to succeed at all costs.

YES

PNK
You're close to your friends, but cold to others.

NO

ARE YOU KIND TO STRANGERS?

YES

OK
You have a lot of heart, which can go a long way!

RACE WITH FRANCESCO

IT IS AN HONOR . . . FOR YOU!

POLE POSITION

1 USE THE COMPLETE PICTURE TO REASSEMBLE THE MIXED-UP SECTIONS AT THE BOTTOM OF THE PAGE AND WRITE THE CORRECT NUMBER NEXT TO EACH SECTION.

1
2
3
4
5
6
7
8

A — 6
B — ...
C — 2
D — ...
E — ...
F — ...
G — ...
H — ...

56

Answers on page 172

INTERNATIONAL FLAGS

FLAGS OF THE US, ITALY, AND JAPAN ARE EACH MISSING A PIECE! FIND THEM FROM THE ONES SHOWN BELOW AND COMPLETE THE NAME OF EACH COUNTRY.

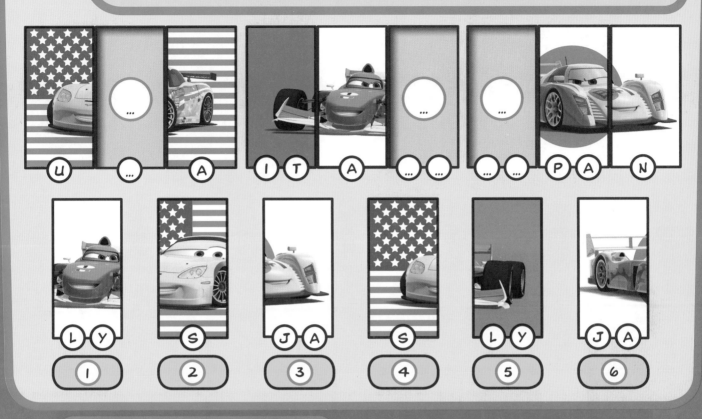

U ... A   I T A ... ... P A N

L Y   S   J A   S   L Y   J A
1   2   3   4   5   6

ADD UP THE TIRES

3

WORK OUT HOW MANY LAPS EACH RACER WILL BE ABLE TO COMPLETE BY ADDING UP THE TOTALS FOR EACH SET OF TIRES. USE THE TIRE KEY TO HELP YOU.

TIRE KEY

SOFT TIRE = 1 LAP   MEDIUM TIRE = 2 LAPS   HARD TIRE = 3 LAPS

2 + ... + ... + ... = ... FRANCESCO

1 + ... + ... + ... = ... NIGEL

... + 3 + ... + ... = ... JEFF

... + ... + 1 + ... = ... RAOUL

MAZE GAME

Woody is leaving Sunnyside and wants to use the kite, but it's difficult to find the way to the roof. Play this maze game with a friend to get Woody safely to the kite on the roof.

FINISH

START

Move right   Move up   Move d

HOW TO PLAY
1) Place a token at each of the two starting points.
2) Roll a die to see how many tiles you can move.
3) Move the token forward on the board in the direction the arrows show.
4) First one to reach the finish—and the kite—wins!

← FINISH

← Move left

START

59

GAME CENTRAL

NOW YOU ARE IN FIX-IT FELIX, JR.!

FIX THE WALL, FELIX!

WRECK-IT RALPH HAS BEEN ON A RAMPAGE! PLAY AS FELIX AND FIX THE WALL BY FILLING EACH HOLE WITH THE CORRECT SHAPE BELOW. WATCH OUT, ONLY SIX SHAPES ARE CORRECT!

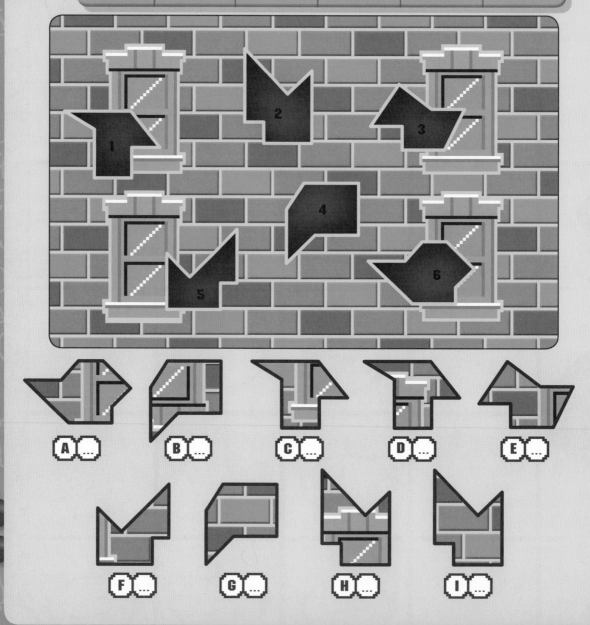

STATION

NOW YOU ARE IN HERO'S DUTY!

FIND THE CY-BUG!

> A CY-BUG IS ABOUT TO ESCAPE! LEAD CALHOUN THROUGH THE UNDERGROUND PIPES TO TAKE IT OUT!

NOW YOU ARE IN SUGAR RUSH!

A MESS OF CANDY!

> VANELLOPE DUMPED OUT A BAG OF CANDY TO FIND SOME RED ONES TO DECORATE HER KART. LOOK THROUGH THE PILE AND PICK OUT THE FIVE RED CANDIES SHOWN BELOW.

61

answers on page 172

DOOFENSHMIRTZ JINGLES INCORPORATED

As any P&F fan knows, the "Doofenshmirtz Evil Incorporated" jingle changes from time to time. Fill in the blanks below with the word from the list at the bottom of the page that correctly completes each Doofenshmirtz jingle.

1) DOOFENSHMIRTZ _____ IN THE SUBURBS

2) DOOFENSHMIRTZ EVIL IS _____

3) DOOFENSHMIRTZ WICKED _____ CASTLE

4) DOOFENSHMIRTZ ABANDONED VACUUM _____ FACTORY

5) DOOFENSHMIRTZ CARBON _____

6) DOOFENSHMIRTZ HIDEOUT-SHAPED _____

YAY! SOMETHING ABOUT *ME!*

FOOTPRINT
HOUSE
ISLAND
CARPETED
WITCH
CLEANER

Answers on page 172

NOW WRITE YOUR OWN JINGLES FOR THESE DOOFENSHMIRTZ SCENES. YOU CAN TEST THEM BY SINGING THEM OUT LOUD!

GOAL STRATEGY

Fethry Duck wants to score a goal! Follow the "strategy" pattern at the bottom to lead him to the net. Watch out—you can't move diagonally!

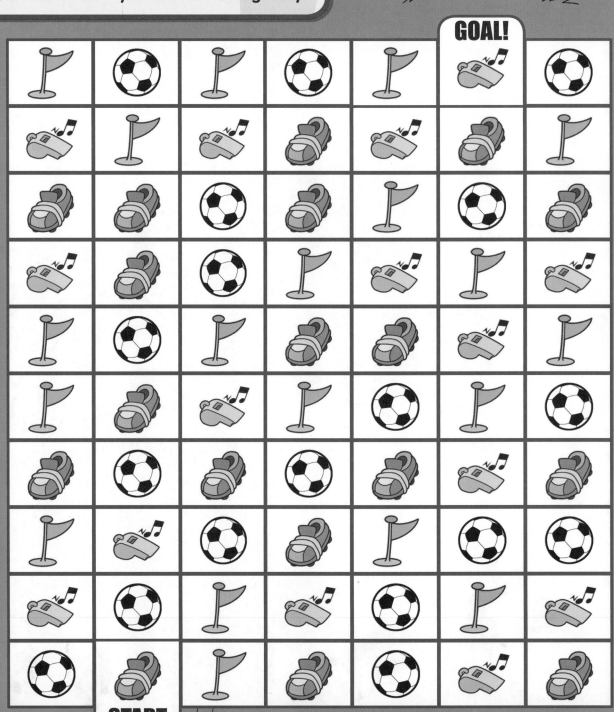

GOAL!

START

Answer on page 172

STRATEGY

PUZZLE STORIES

The six pictures of this story are all mixed up! Put them in the right order, but be careful— one of them doesn't belong in the story!

B

1

2

C

3

4

PASSES

Are you ready to practice your game strategy? Complete the sequence of passes and win the game!

 2   **4**   **6**   **8**   **12**

65

Answers on page 172

NIGHTMARE TEAM

Who would be on your "dream team" to conquer the Scare Games events? Check out all the students on these pages and choose your favorite six monsters for the competition!

RΩR

JOHNNY WORTHINGTON
Big, smart, and scary; MU's top scaring student.

PNK

CRYSTAL DU BOIS
Smart, fast, and can see in the dark.

HSS

NANCY KIM
Her "evil eye" maneuver can scare from 100 feet away.

RΩR

RANDY BOGGS
Lacks self-confidence. Can turn invisible.

OK

SCOTT "SQUISHY" SQUIBBLES
Tiny and silent, he can sneak up on anyone, anywhere.

ΣΣK

CARLA DELGADO
Amphibious and athletic, there's nowhere she can't go.

RΩR

CHET ALEXANDER
Fast, loud, and unpredictable.

HSS

RHONDA BOYD
Has whips for hair and a scream that turns food rotten.

TOXICITY CHALLENGE
Race through a dark sewer tunnel—watch out for toxic urchins!

1

AVOID THE PARENT
Grab your flag and escape the library—quietly! Don't alert the terrifying librarian!

2

JAMES P. "SULLEY" SULLIVAN
A talented Scarer, but doesn't care about strategy.

SUSAN JENSEN
Raised by circus performers, she's incredibly agile.

OMAR HARRIS
Small and aerodynamic, he's a master of the flying dive-bomb.

BRYNN LARSON
Fast on her feet, with three eyes that see everything.

DONNA SOOHOO
Where is her face? Nobody knows, and that's terrifying!

BRITNEY DAVIS
So loud that her shriek can break glass.

MIKE WAZOWSKI
Knows everything about scaring. But is he really scary?

ROY "BIG RED" O'GROWLAHAN
Strong as 10 oxen, with a temper to match.

DON'T SCARE THE TEEN
Scare the kids in the maze, but steer clear of the teenagers!

3

BABOSO GORETEGA
Can squish his body through a hole of any size.

NAOMI JACKSON
Merciless and telepathic.

SIMULATED SCARE
The main event—scare the child to collect the most scream energy!

5

HIDE AND SNEAK
Hide in the house and avoid the flashlights of the referees!

4

NEW FRIENDS

68

LOOK! ATTIC!

DOES BONNIE REALLY WANT TO SEND US TO THE ATTIC?

DON'T WORRY! YOU'VE MISUNDERSTOOD!

THE BOX IS FULL! SOMEONE CALLED JANET HAS GIVEN HER OLD TOYS TO BONNIE!

MAYBE THERE ARE NEW FRIENDS IN THE BOX!

SO . . . WHY AREN'T THEY COMING OUT?

THEY MIGHT BE FRIGHTENED! A HEARTY WELCOME'S REQUIRED!

THE CHAIR IS VERY HIGH! HOW CAN WE CLIMB UP THERE?

NO PROBLEM, SHERIFF!

ATTIC

69

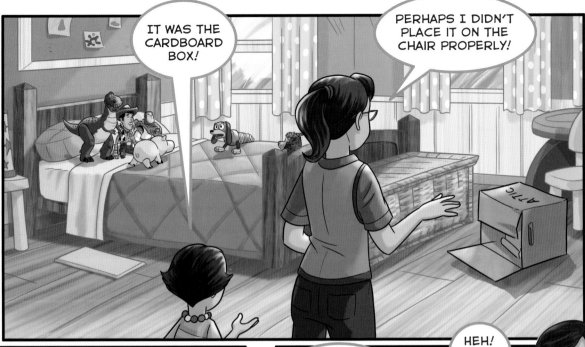

IT WAS THE CARDBOARD BOX!

PERHAPS I DIDN'T PLACE IT ON THE CHAIR PROPERLY!

I FINISHED MY DINNER, MOM!

CAN I LOOK AT MY NEW BOOKS NOW?

HEH! HEH! OK!

LOOK! HERE'S THE STORY OF THE THREE LITTLE PIGS!

BOOKS ARE GREAT FRIENDS, TOO!

WOODY WAS RIGHT. NOTHING TO WORRY ABOUT!

THE END

TOP SECRET

GOOD MORNING, AGENT . . . AGENT . . . WELL, LET'S JUST CALL YOU AGENT R!

THAT'S "R" FOR "READER"!

I'M MAJOR MONOGRAM OF THE OWCA.

THAT'S THE "ORGANIZATION WITHOUT A COOL ACRONYM"!

CARL!

SORRY, SIR!

WHERE WAS I? RIGHT. IF YOU'RE GOING TO BE A PART OF THE TEAM, YOU NEED TO KNOW ALL ABOUT OUR BEST OPERATIVE, AGENT P. STUDY THIS FILE CAREFULLY—OR YOU'LL END UP LIKE CARL!

Agent P

aka Perry the Platypus, household pet and secret agent.

Description: Though his owners think this semiaquatic, egg-laying mammal is nothing more than an average platypus (they don't do much), Perry is in reality a world-class secret agent. Accomplished in many forms of hand-to-hand combat, Agent P has thwarted Dr. Doofenshmirtz more than one hundred times.

Distinguishing features: Wall-eyed stare (in pet mode), ready-for-action look, fedora (in agent mode).

Known to say: "Brbrbrbrbrbr."

Phineas Flynn

"Owner" and closest family member to Agent P, aka Perry the Platypus.

Description: Phineas is a curious, positive, and creative kid whose main goal in life is to have the best summer ever, and he is constantly inventing new adventures to achieve that goal.

Distinguishing features: Triangular head, tuft of red hair, sunny disposition.

Known to say: "Ferb, I know what we're gonna do today!" and "Oh, there you are, Perry."

Sneak a peek at Agent P's OWCA file and learn all about your favorite *Phineas and Ferb* characters!

Ferb Fletcher

Stepbrother to Phineas.

Description: Ferb is a man of action rather than words. But what he lacks as a conversationalist he makes up for in brilliance and resourcefulness, and he's always an instrumental part of Phineas' summer schemes.

Distinguishing features: English accent, wide-ranging vocabulary, remarkable engineering skills.

Known to say: Not much, but when he does, it's something unusual.

73

Candace Flynn

Sister to Phineas, stepsister to Ferb.

Description: Some might call Candace a typical teenage girl: she loves the mall and mushy stories (like *The Princess Sensibilities*), and she's obsessed with her crush—and busting her younger brothers.

Distinguishing features: Long red hair, googly-eyed look when in the presence of her crush, Jeremy.

Known to say: "Mom, Mom, look what Phineas and Ferb are doing!"

Dr. Heinz Doofenshmirtz

Mad scientist and arch-nemesis of Agent P.

Description: To call Dr. Doofenshmirtz an evil genius would be half right. He invents an astounding array of devices (or "Inators," such as the Destruct-Inator) meant to wreak havoc in the Tri-State area, but somehow they always come up short when put into practice.

Distinguishing features: Ever-present white lab coat, maniacal gleam in his eye.

Known to say: "Curse you, Perry the Platypus!"

Isabella Garcia-Shapiro

Smart and resourceful, Isabella has a crush on Phineas. She and her fellow Fireside Girls often assist Phineas and Ferb in their adventures.

Jeremy Johnson

Candace's crush/boyfriend/light-of-her-life is a sweet, laid-back teen who plays the guitar and works at Mr. Slushy Burger. His little sister, Suzy, on the other hand, has it in for Candace.

Lawrence Fletcher

aka Dad. Linda's husband, Lawrence, often stumbles upon his sons in the midst of one of their projects, but he assumes that they must have their mom's permission and happily cheers them on.

Linda Flynn

aka Mom. Mom is ever-busy and ever-clueless about her sons' amazing activities, such as building a roller coaster or a flying car.

OTHER NOTABLE CONTACTS

Buford Van Stomm

Some people are afraid of Buford (who lives by the Bully Code), but he's protective of Baljeet and sometimes joins Phineas and Ferb in their adventures. Just don't let him near a wedgie machine.

Baljeet Rai

One of Phineas and Ferb's friends, Baljeet is polite, mild-mannered, and in constant pursuit of good grades. Did we say "good" grades? We meant the best grades ever.

JAM-MATER ROCKS OUT

76

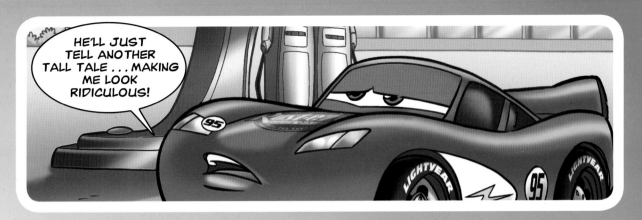

HE'LL JUST TELL ANOTHER TALL TALE . . . MAKING ME LOOK RIDICULOUS!

OH, HAVE A LITTLE FAITH! COME ON, MATER, LET'S HEAR ALL ABOUT IT!

I HAD MY OWN BAND AND A HEAP O' FANS!

"OUR SHOWS SOLD OUT STADIUMS EVERYWHERE! MY STAGE NAME WAS . . . "

JAM-ATER JAM-ATER!

THIS NEXT NUMBER IS MY BIGGEST HIT!

DAD GUM! DAD GUM! DAD GUM ROCK!

YEEAH!

DAD GUM!

"DAD GUM ROCK"?! COME ON, YOU'RE MAKING THIS UP!

AM NOT! AND YOU SHOULD KNOW . . .

" . . . 'CAUSE YOU WERE THERE!"

BRROOAAMM

JAM OUT, DUDE!

DAD GUM ROOOCK!

"AFTER ME, YOU WERE THE BIGGEST ATTRACTION IN HEAVY METAL!"

JAM-ATER! JAM-ATER!

LIGHTNING McQUEEN! LIGHTNING McQUEEN!

I KNEW IT! HERE COMES THE PART WHERE I FALL FLAT ON MY FENDER.

NO, NO! YOU WERE A HUGE HIT . . .

" . . . ESPECIALLY WITH THE GIRLS!"

WE LOVE YOU, LIGHTNING McQUEEN!

WE COULD LISTEN TO YOUR ENGINE ROAR ALL DAY LONG!

HEE! HEE! LEAVE ONE FOR ME, SUPERSTAR!

The End

"Secrets from the OWCA: The Organization Without a Cool Acronym"

THE END

EXPLORE THE MU CAMPUS

Use this handy map to find your way through MU.
Take a closer look to spot the places listed below.
Can you find them all in one minute?

MONSTERS UNIVERSITY

 ✓ School of Aviation

 ✓ Registration Hall

 ✓ JOX Fraternity House

 ✓ Amphitheater

 ✓ School of Engineering

 ✓ Troll Bridge

 ✓ Clock Tower

Answers on page 172

THE SECRET DEVICES

SECRET DEVICES

1	✓
2	✓
3	✓
4	✓
5	✓
6	✓
7	✓
8	✓
9	✓
10	✓
11	✓
12	✓
13	✓
14	✓
15	✓
16	✓
17	✓
18	✓
19	✓
20	✓
21	✓
22	✓
TOTAL	
....	

HELP MATER REACH FINN McMISSILE AT THE END OF THE MAZE WHILE COLLECTING AS MANY **SECRET DEVICES** AS YOU CAN! USE A PENCIL AND MOVE HORIZONTALLY OR VERTICALLY, BUT DO NOT PASS THE SAME BLOCK TWICE!

FORBIDDEN!

MATER

PASSWORD?

START

AFTER YOU REACH FINN, COUNT YOUR SECRET DEVICES.

FEWER THAN 11: NOT BAD

12-17: GOOD

18-22: EXCELLENT

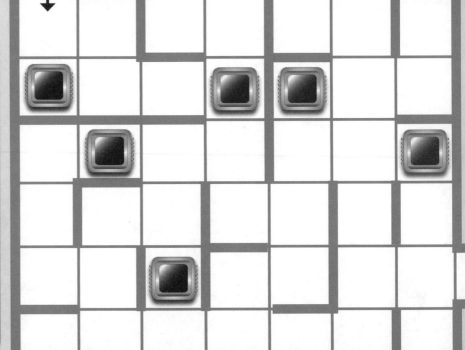

84

Answer on page 172

FINISH

BRILLIANT, AGENT MATER!

FINN McMISSILE

85

Donald Duck

LET'S GET STARTED!

Donald Duck is four times as tall as his head. Keep in mind that the neck (1) gets thinner as it nears the body, and that the body (2) is pear-shaped and curved. Once you have drawn these elements, move to the arms (3) by sketching two thin pipes thickening at the wrists. Do the same for the legs (4), which are shorter. Don't forget the tail (5) placed at the middle of his rear end.

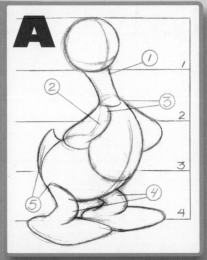

Donald Duck's hand is as big as his head (1). If you look closely at his fingers, you'll notice they are thin, flexible, and . . . as soft as a feather (2). Remember that, unlike Mickey Mouse, Donald doesn't wear gloves so his hands and fingers are not as big as Mickey's (3).

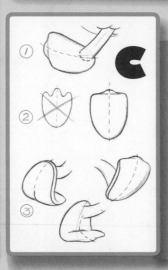

Donald Duck's feet are flat. Draw the ankles (1) at a short distance from the heel. The foot makes a soft curve and only the middle toe (2) sticks out a little. If you decide to show the sole, add some slight thickness (3).

Be careful how you attach the legs to the body— position them at the sides, toward the rear of the body, and well apart from one another.

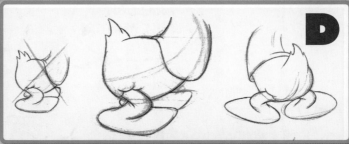

2

DETAILS & POSES

Donald Duck's jacket has a collar (1) encircling the neck and coming down all the way along the back. Draw the sleeves (2) as you would two cones ending with colored stripes, positioned at two fingers' distance from the hem. The bow tie (3) is soft and "full"—put it on top of the neck opening.

E

When drawing Donald Duck, make sure not to hide important parts of his body. With each posture, aim to draw both the hands and feet and keep the hat, beak, and tail visible.

G

F

If you want to have fun and exaggerate Donald's moods, accentuate the curved line as your guide for his body. Be careful with the clothes; have them fit the body in a natural, soft way.

H

Donald Duck's body always follows a curved line, allowing him to express his mood. If you want him to be excited and happy, draw him leaning forward. To express different attitudes, try other kinds of curves. Try the straight line as well— it conveys surprise or fright.

SCARE UP YOUR SCHEDULE

HOW WILL YOU FILL YOUR DAY AT MONSTERS UNIVERSITY?

Every day at MU is full of classes and clubs! To fill out your daily schedule, roll a die to add the class or club from the corresponding lists below to your schedule on the right!

CLASS LIST

- **FUZZY MATH**
- **ART OF SCREAM CAN CONSTRUCTION**
- **MONSTERS' LIT**
- **FLYING FOR WINGED MONSTERS**
- **CITY PLANNING**
- **CITY DESTROYING**

CLUB LIST

- **BOOKWORMS' CLUB**
  DISCUSSION OF *SLIME AND PUNISHMENT*
- **ART CLUB**
  PAINTING, POTTERY, AND INTERPRETIVE BELCHING
- **DEBATE TEAM**
  PRACTICE FOR MONSTER MELEE SEMIFINALS
- **THE CAMPUS ROAR**
  OFFICIAL NEWSPAPER OF MONSTERS UNIVERSITY
- **SCARE DEMOS**
  PRACTICE THE "JOHNSON CRACKLE AND HOWL" MANEUVER
- **DRAMA CLUB**
  REHEARSAL FOR *MY SCARE LADY*

MONSTERS
— UNIVERSITY —

TODAY'S SCHEDULE

9 a.m.	**SCARING 101**
10:30 a.m.	.... Roll a die to choose from **CLASS LIST**
12 p.m.	**LUNCH AT THE GROWL** Today's special: chili cheese flies
1:30 p.m.	.... Roll a die to choose from **CLASS LIST**
3 p.m.	**INTRODUCTION TO SLIMEOLOGY**
4:30 p.m.	.... Roll a die to choose from **CLUB LIST**
6 p.m.	**DINNER AT THE GROWL** Today's special: All-you-can-eat hot sludge sundaes
7 p.m.	.... Roll a die to choose from **CLUB LIST**

Homework

Scare Games
Prep

To-Do Lists

UNUSUAL PENALTY

Arrange the five picture scenes in the correct order to see what kind of funny penalty shot Goofy is taking!

ANSWER:
◯ ◯ ◯ ◯ ◯

SUPER DRIBBLING

Starting from the START, go toward the GOAL. Keep in mind that you must touch all the balls, but you can touch each ball only once and you can only move one number up or down!

Answers on page 172

FIND THE WAY

Help Donald Duck find the right way through the maze of streets to get to the stadium for the soccer game!

START

313

FINISH

It's your turn to fix it!

NOW YOU ARE IN FIX–IT FELIX, JR.!

WORD WRECK

RALPH DEMOLISHED THIS WALL OF WORDS, AND NOW THE LETTERS
ARE ALL MIXED UP! CAN YOU UNSCRAMBLE EACH WORD?

Ⓐ _ _ _ _ _

Ⓑ _ _ _ _ _

Ⓒ _ _ _ _ _

Ⓓ _ _ _ _ _ _ _ _

Ⓔ _ _ _ _ _

Ⓕ _ _ _ _ _

Ⓖ _ _ _ _ _ _

Ⓗ _ _ _ _

Ⓘ _ _ _ _ _ _ _

Ⓐ GUSRA

Ⓑ NYACD

Ⓒ RCEKW

Ⓓ ALINECDN

Ⓔ CRAER

Ⓕ EELLV

Ⓖ MHAREM

Ⓗ EOHR

Ⓘ ROIDSLE

Answers on page 172

EXTREME CLOSE-UP

THE GAME WORLD LOOKS A LOT DIFFERENT WHEN YOU'RE THE SIZE OF A BABY CY-BUG! EACH OF THESE IMAGES IS A SUPER CLOSE-UP LOOK AT SOMETHING FROM HERO'S DUTY. CAN YOU FIGURE OUT WHAT THEY ARE?

A ....

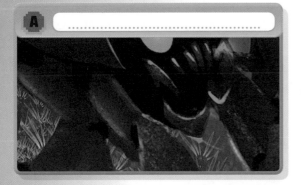

B ....

C ....

D ....

E ....

F ....

COLOR MASH-UP

Look at this picture of Woody's friends.
Something's not quite right with the colors.
Can you find five things that are the wrong color?

94

Answers on page 17

THE RIGHT HAT

Whoops, where did Woody's and Jessie's hats go?
Help them find the right ones!

A

B

C

D

E

F

NAPKIN DOG

So, what did you do with BONNIE today?

Uh . . . we just played TEA PARTY!

WOW! It's so much fun!

Well . . . this time it was kind of BORING!

I was the napkin HOLDER!

?!

Answers on page 172

FAST DRAWING

COPY
THE DRAWING
OF FRANCESCO
BERNOULLI
BELOW.
TIP:
USE THE
SQUARES AS
A GUIDE.

YOU ARE VERY GOOD-LOOKING!

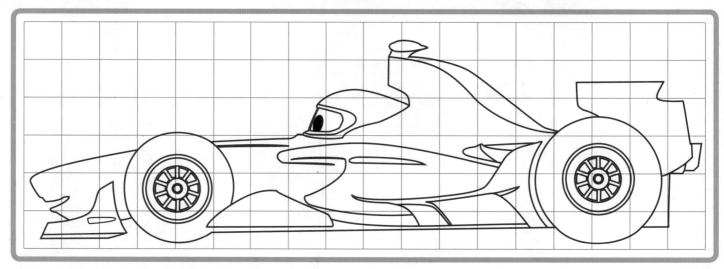

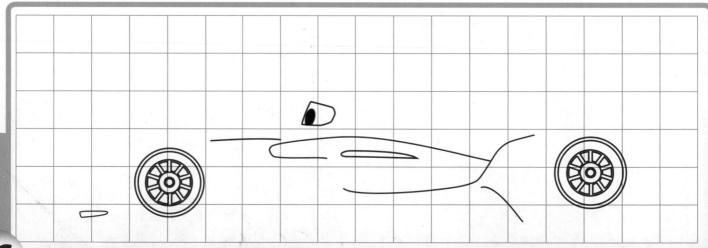

SUPER SECRET HIDE-AND-SEEK!

RADIATOR SPRINGS. MATER'S PLAYING HIDE-AND-SEEK WITH HIS FRIENDS . . .

. . . TWENTY-THREE, TWENTY-FOUR, TWENTY-FIVE!

READY OR NOT, HERE I COME!

FOUND YOU!

I TOLD YOU IT WASN'T A GOOD PLACE!

FOUND YOU!

WHAT?

FOUND YOU!

HEY . . . YOU'RE A **WIZARD**, MY FRIEND!

FOUND YOU, TOO!

ARGH! I CAN'T BELIEVE IT!

HA! HA! I WON! I'VE NEVER WON AT HIDE-AND-SEEK BEFORE!

IF I KNEW YOU NEEDED IT FOR THIS, I WOULD NEVER HAVE LOANED YOU OUR **SUPER SATELLITE SEEKER**, MATER!

The End

One night at a restaurant, Dan Povenmire drew a triangle-headed kid on the butcher-paper tablecloth—the blueprint for Phineas.

Inside an EVIL MIND
The Dr. Wexler Story

Povenmire and Marsh pitched the *Phineas and Ferb* series concept for 14 years before landing at the Disney Channel.

PHASCINATING PHACTS

The Giant Floating Baby Head has appeared in seven *Phineas and Ferb* episodes! Phineas and Ferb aren't totally sure where he comes from.

PERRY

All the main characters are based on geometric shapes: Phineas is a triangle, Ferb is a rectangle, Candace and Isabella are half circles.

Candace only plays instruments that start with "B": bass, banjo, bassoon, bagpipes, bongos, and the balalaika (a stringed instrument of Russian origin).

Each character was crafted to be recognizable from a distance or in silhouette.

Dr. Doofenshmirtz's greatest hero in all of evil science is Dr. Lloyd Wexler, author of *Inside an Evil Mind*.

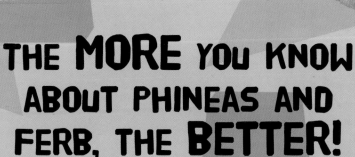

THE **MORE** YOU KNOW ABOUT PHINEAS AND FERB, THE **BETTER!**

You can't have a pet Perry. Platypuses are native Australian animals, protected by law. They are not allowed to be kept as pets in Australia or in any other country.

The creators of *Phineas and Ferb*, Dan Povenmire and Jeff "Swampy" Marsh, were drawn into the episode "Dude, We're Getting the Band Back Together!" as members of the band "Love Händel".

Phineas, Ferb, and Candace's mom is based on Dan's real-life sister, Linda, whom he describes as an absolutely unflappable super-mom raising really smart, creative kids.

FAMILY SIZE

THE END

A WORK OF ART

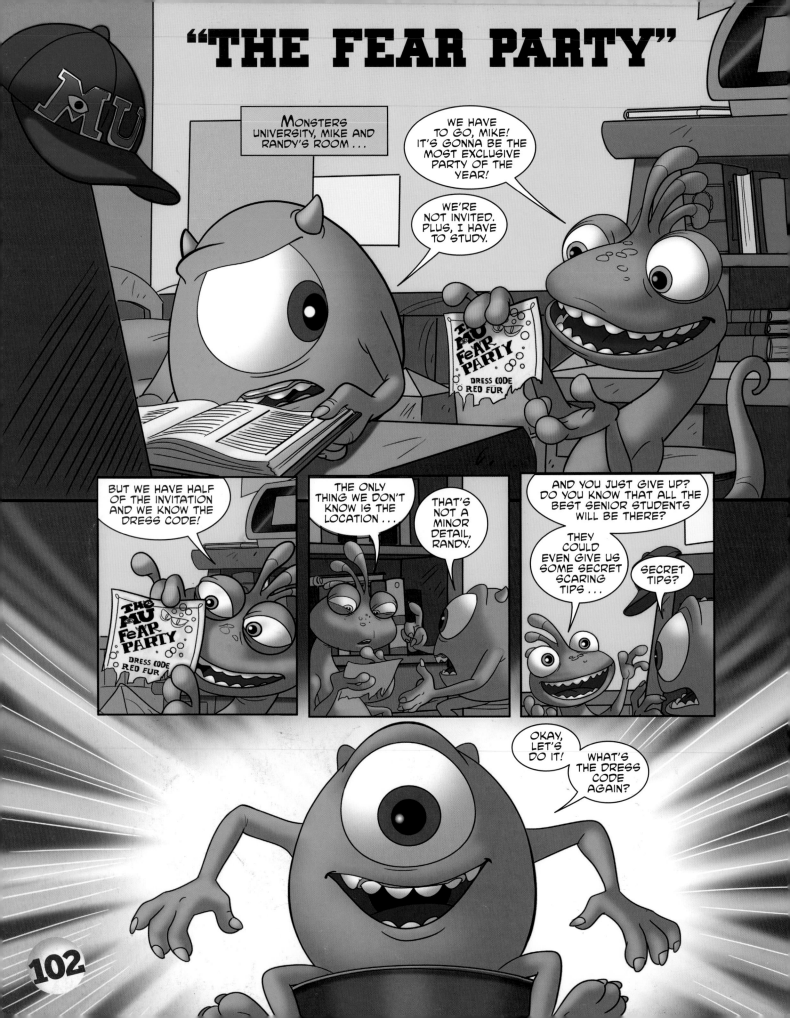

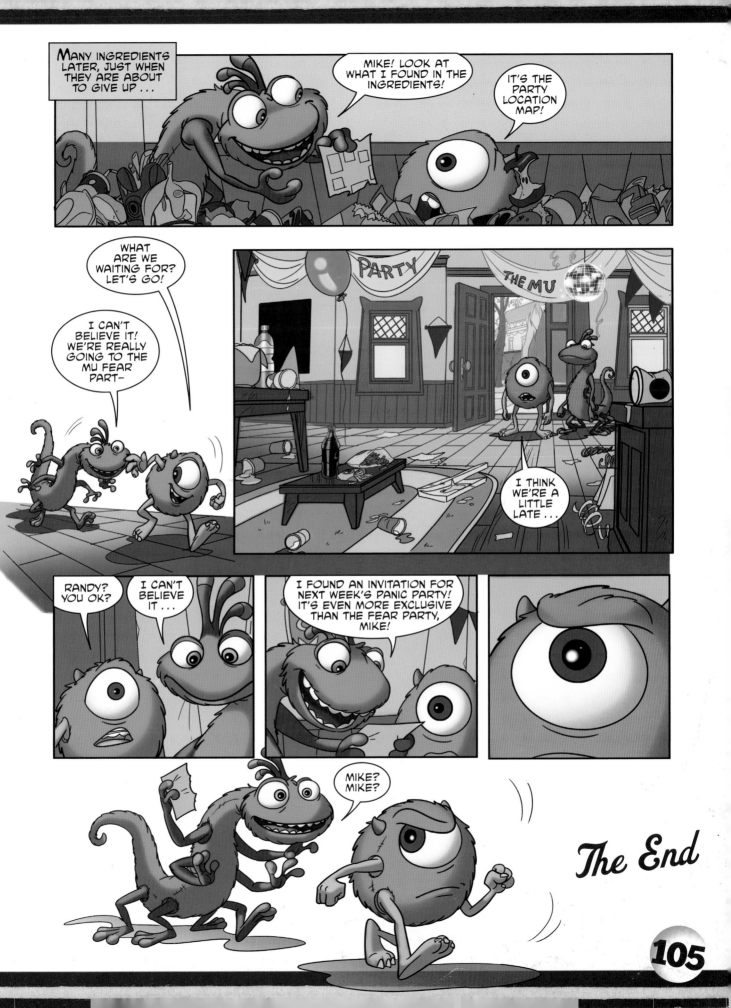

The End

PLUTO'S SURPRISE PACKAGE

I'M OFF TO TOWN TO PAY THE RENT, PLUTO! IF THE MAILMAN COMES, TAKE CARE OF THE BIKE HELMET I ORDERED FOR MINNIE!

GNIK GNIK GNIK

IH, IH, IH!

?

WROOM

A DIFFERENT KIND OF RACE!

SPEED! I AM SPEED!

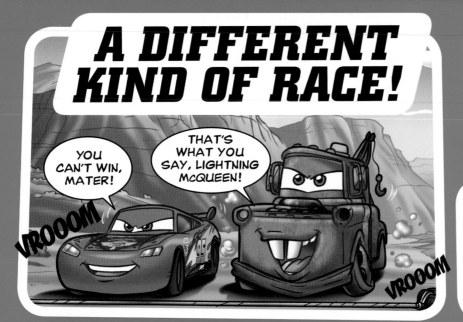

YOU CAN'T WIN, MATER!

THAT'S WHAT YOU SAY, LIGHTNING McQUEEN!

THAT'S YOUR PROBLEM, BUDDY!

OKAY, PIPE DOWN! READY?

SET . . . GO!

LIGHTNING McQUEEN MOVED! THE FIRST STANDING-STILL WORLD CHAMPIONSHIP GOES TO . . . MATER!

NUTS! I TRAINED SO HARD FOR THIS ONE . . .

OH, YEAH! I'M THE CHAMP! I'M THE CHAMP!

The End

Laundry Day

The End

RECYCLED CAR

Respect trees, everybody. Save paper!

YOU'LL NEED:

TIP ASK AN ADULT TO HELP YOU!

- A PAPER TOWEL TUBE • CARDBOARD (FROM A SHOEBOX IS PERFECT)
- A STRAW (ONLY THE LONGEST PART, CUT IN TWO EQUAL PARTS)
- A SHEET OF COLORED PAPER • COLORED FELT-TIP PENS
- ROUND-TIP SCISSORS • COLORED ADHESIVE TAPE • STRONG GLUE

1

USE PENS AND TAPE TO DECORATE A PAPER-TOWEL TUBE (SEE EXAMPLE).

TIP
YOU CAN COVER THE ENTIRE TUBE WITH DIFFERENT COLORED TAPE. IF YOU LIKE, ADD FLAMES OR NUMBERS ON THE SIDES.

2

CUT OUT TWO CARDBOARD DISKS ABOUT 4 INCHES IN DIAMETER, AND TWO CARDBOARD DISKS ABOUT 2.5 INCHES IN DIAMETER. COLOR THEM ANY WAY YOU LIKE.

2.5 INCHES

SPOILER FLAP

5.5 INCHES

SPOILER WINGS

3

TO MAKE THE SPOILER, CUT OUT THREE PIECES OF CARDBOARD, AS SHOWN. FOLD ALONG THE DOTTED LINES.

FOLD   FOLD

4.5 INCHES

FOLD   FOLD

4 INCHES   2.5 INCHES

2.5 INCHES

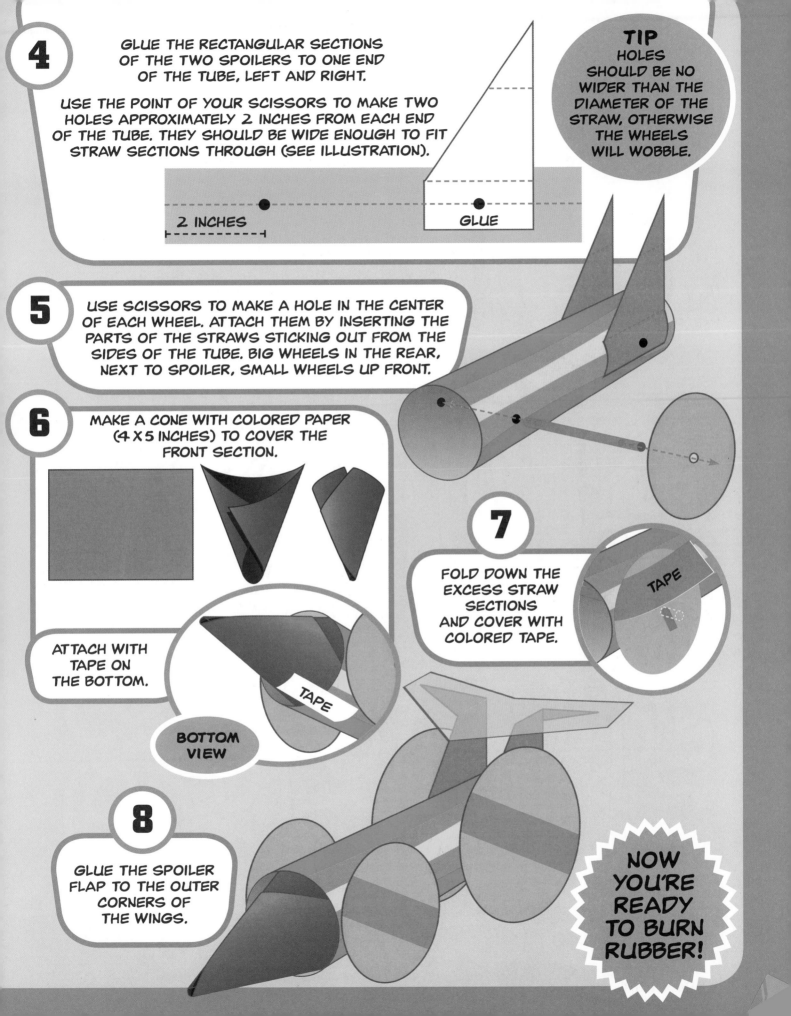

4 GLUE THE RECTANGULAR SECTIONS OF THE TWO SPOILERS TO ONE END OF THE TUBE, LEFT AND RIGHT.

USE THE POINT OF YOUR SCISSORS TO MAKE TWO HOLES APPROXIMATELY 2 INCHES FROM EACH END OF THE TUBE. THEY SHOULD BE WIDE ENOUGH TO FIT STRAW SECTIONS THROUGH (SEE ILLUSTRATION).

2 INCHES

GLUE

TIP HOLES SHOULD BE NO WIDER THAN THE DIAMETER OF THE STRAW, OTHERWISE THE WHEELS WILL WOBBLE.

5 USE SCISSORS TO MAKE A HOLE IN THE CENTER OF EACH WHEEL. ATTACH THEM BY INSERTING THE PARTS OF THE STRAWS STICKING OUT FROM THE SIDES OF THE TUBE. BIG WHEELS IN THE REAR, NEXT TO SPOILER, SMALL WHEELS UP FRONT.

6 MAKE A CONE WITH COLORED PAPER (4 X 5 INCHES) TO COVER THE FRONT SECTION.

ATTACH WITH TAPE ON THE BOTTOM.

TAPE

BOTTOM VIEW

7 FOLD DOWN THE EXCESS STRAW SECTIONS AND COVER WITH COLORED TAPE.

TAPE

8 GLUE THE SPOILER FLAP TO THE OUTER CORNERS OF THE WINGS.

NOW YOU'RE READY TO BURN RUBBER!

MONSTER BRAIN GAMES

Use your monster skills to solve these puzzles!

1 WHERE'S THE SCHOOL OF SCARING?

It can be tricky to find the right building on campus! Help Mike find the correct path to reach the School of Scaring.

TROLL BRIDGE

SCHOOL OF DOOR TECH.

DORMITORY

Answer on page 172

SCHOOL OF SCARING

CHET'S SHADOW

2 Can you guess which of the four shadows perfectly matches the picture below?

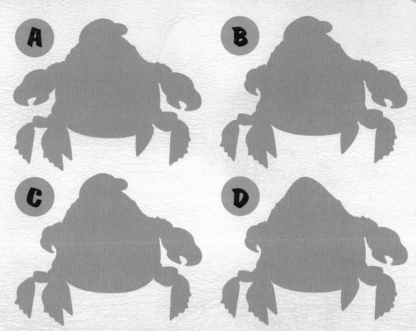

A

B

C

D

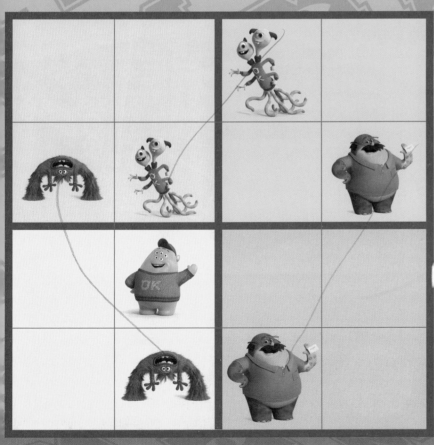

MONSTER SUDOKU

3 Each row, column, and each of the four large squares should contain all four MU students.

MONSTER FEET

YOU'LL NEED:

- 2 EMPTY TISSUE BOXES
- 1 SHEET OF CARDBOARD APPROXIMATELY 14 X 20 INCHES
- GLUE • FELT-TIP PENS,
- ACRYLIC PAINTS
- 1 PAINTBRUSH • SAFETY SCISSORS

1

COLOR THE TWO BOXES ANY WAY YOU LIKE TO CREATE FRONT AND REAR CAR SECTIONS ON EACH.

2

ON CARDBOARD, DRAW, COLOR, AND CUT OUT EIGHT WHEELS APPROXIMATELY 4 INCHES IN DIAMETER. YOU MAY WANT TO CUT TREADS IN THEM, AS SHOWN IN FIGURE B.

X 8

B

3

GLUE WHEELS ONTO BOTH BOXES, SO THAT THEY EXTEND PAST TOP AND BOTTOM EDGES.

4

CUT AWAY EXTENDED AREAS OF WHEELS ON THE LOWER EDGES, MAKING THEM LEVEL WITH THE BOTTOMS OF THE BOXES.

5

CUT OUT SMALL CARDBOARD TRIANGLES, COLOR THEM IN AND THEN GLUE THEM ONTO THE FRONT OF EACH MONSTER FOOT SO THEY LOOK LIKE CLAWS!

YOUR MONSTER FEET ARE READY TO WEAR.

MAKE SURE YOU DON'T SCARE THE OTHER SHOES IN YOUR ROOM!

WOW! VERY SCARY!

SCARER OF THE MONTH

Grab a friend for this race across the Scare Floor!

START

YOU WILL NEED: One die, and a token for each player.

TO PLAY: Each player places his or her token on START. The youngest player begins by rolling the die and traveling that many spaces. The player should follow any instructions on the space where he or she lands. Then the next player takes a turn. The first player to reach Boo's door wins!

You slip on a banana peel and make a kid laugh.

GO AHEAD 3 SPACES.

TAKE A SHORTCUT THROUGH THE CLOSET!

YOU SCARE A WHOLE SLUMBER PARTY! GO AHEAD 1 SPACE.

CHANGE PLACES WITH ANY MONSTER ON THE BOARD

You forget to file your paperwork.

LOSE A TURN.

You fill five scream canisters.

GO AHEAD 1 SPACE.

TAKE A SHORTCUT THROUGH THE **CLOSET!**

A sock is stuck to your back! **GO BACK 2 SPACES.**

You tell a funny joke and get a big laugh!

GO AHEAD 5 SPACES.

TAKE A SHORTCUT THROUGH THE **CLOSET!**

You forget to close the closet door behind you. **GO BACK TO START.**

FINISH

121

REX-O-LETTERS

Rex begins with R! Circle all the Rs below and count them.

OOOO, R-E-X— THAT'S ME!

MISSION ACCOMPLISHED!

COLOR WHEN FINISHED

WORDS IN THE DARK

I LIKE THIS PLACE! IT'S BIG AND COLORFUL AND . . .

HMM . . . MAYBE I KNOW HOW TO STOP HIM . . .

IF WE PLAY HIDE-AND-SEEK, HE'LL HAVE TO BE QUIET!

HEY! WHEN ARE YOU GUYS GONNA FIND ME? DO YOU NEED A HINT? . . . BLAH, BLAH . . .

SIGH!

123

Answer on page 172

Snack time!

Goofy loves snack time! Especially when the snack is a hotdog. Here he is on a rainy day with a yummy snack. Find three things in each of his shadows that have disappeared. Circle them when you find them.

Bag lifting

Donald Duck has to accompany Daisy Duck shopping and, knowing how many bags he'll have to carry, is training hard. Do you want to see him train? Color all the spaces marked by a dot.

Answers on page 173

Money maker

Uncle Scrooge is busy with his favorite pastime—making money! And he's so absorbed in what he's doing that he hasn't even noticed that some things have disappeared! There are five differences between the two pictures below. Can you find them all? Circle them when you do.

Refreshing dessert

On a hot day, Donald loves to cool down with a cool ice pop. He has gotten a bit carried away with choosing his ice pop and picked up too many. How many do you think there are? Can you guess whether there are more than 30 without counting?

125

nswers on page 173

FOR FANS ONLY

ANTENNA BALLS!

1

MISSING PIECES

THIS PICTURE OF THE KING, CHICK HICKS, AND LIGHTNING IS MISSING SIX PIECES. DRAW A LINE FROM EACH PIECE TO ITS CORRECT PLACE IN THE PICTURE.

BRIAN

Answers on page 173

2 FANS' LOOKS

THERE'S NO MISTAKING A TRUE FAN!
MATCH EACH FAN TO HIS SHADOW.

CORIANDER
WIDETRACK (A)

ALBERT
HINKEY (B)

LUIGI (C)

CONVOY
BROTHER (D)

| (1) ... | (2) ... | (3) ... | (4) ... |

3

A FAN'S FLAG

COLOR IN
THE SPACES WITH
DOTS TO FIND
OUT WHICH LOGO
APPEARS ON
MATTHEW'S FLAG.

MATTHEW
TRUE BLUE

(A)   (B)   (C)

127

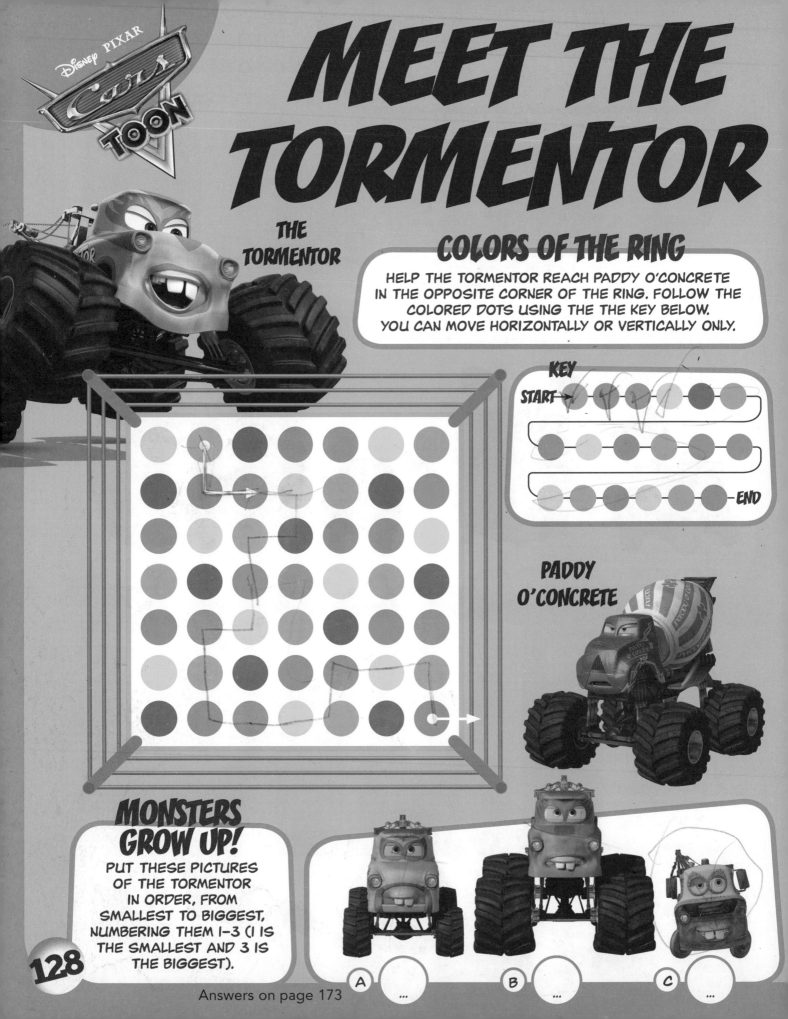

MEET THE TORMENTOR

THE TORMENTOR

COLORS OF THE RING

HELP THE TORMENTOR REACH PADDY O'CONCRETE IN THE OPPOSITE CORNER OF THE RING. FOLLOW THE COLORED DOTS USING THE THE KEY BELOW. YOU CAN MOVE HORIZONTALLY OR VERTICALLY ONLY.

KEY

START →

END

PADDY O'CONCRETE

MONSTERS GROW UP!

PUT THESE PICTURES OF THE TORMENTOR IN ORDER, FROM SMALLEST TO BIGGEST, NUMBERING THEM 1-3 (1 IS THE SMALLEST AND 3 IS THE BIGGEST).

A ...

B ...

C ...

128

Answers on page 173

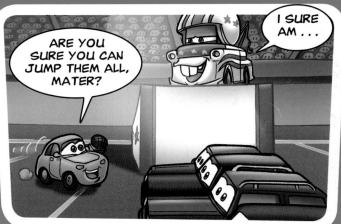

"THE GLOVE CHALLENGE"

MONSTERS UNIVERSITY. MIKE WAZOWSKI IS GOING TO HIS FIRST CLASS OF THE DAY . . .

WHEN . . .

WHA . . .!?

THERE'S A HUMAN GLOVE ON THE FLOOR!

ONE MINUTE LATER, EVERY MONSTER IN THE DORM IS THERE!

I CAN TOUCH IT . . . I'M NOT AFRAID OF IT!

EASY THERE, LITTLE GUY. LET A MONSTER WITH REAL SCARE POTENTIAL TAKE CARE OF THIS!

SO TOUCH IT! I DARE YOU!

AND I DOUBLE DARE YOU!

GENTLEMEN, ARE YOU NOT UP TO THE CHALLENGE?

OKAY, THEN.

LET'S DO IT.

YOU'VE FOUND IT!

?

MY HAT! I WAS LOOKING FOR IT EVERYWHERE!

The End

A DIRTY TRICK

A NEW RACE IS ABOUT TO BEGIN ...

LIGHTNING McQUEEN! TODAY'S RACE PUTS YOU AGAINST CHICK HICKS! ARE YOU UP TO THE TEST?

CHICK IS A WORTHY OPPONENT! IT'S GOING TO BE ROUGH OUT THERE!

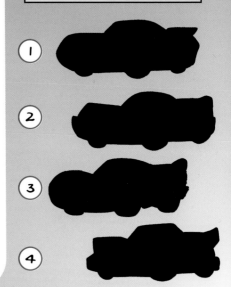

WHICH ONE OF THESE SILHOUETTES MATCHES LIGHTNING'S SHAPE AS IT APPEARS ON THE LEFT?

1
2
3
4

NOT FAR AWAY ...

I'M SURE TO WIN TODAY'S RACE! YOU KNOW WHAT YOU HAVE TO DO?

OF COURSE! I SPILL OIL ON THE THIRD TURN!

RIGHT! I'LL GET THAT BLOCKHEAD LIGHTNING McQUEEN TO RIDE OVER IT— HE'LL SPIN OUT AND I'LL WIN!

CHEATERS! THEY NEED TO BE TAUGHT A LESSON!

Answer on page 173

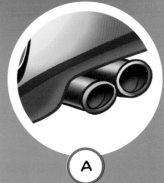

A

B

C

D

WHICH OF THESE OBJECTS AND DETAILS DOES NOT BELONG TO LIGHTNING?

133

Answer on page 173

LIGHTNING McQUEEN TAKES THE **LEAD**, BUT CHICK HICKS IS RIGHT **BEHIND** HIM!

HEE, HEE! HAVE **FUN** WHILE YOU CAN! YOU'RE IN FOR A BIG **SURPRISE!**

THE RACERS APPROACH THE **THIRD TURN!**

OKAY! THIS IS IT!

IF WE DON'T DO SOMETHING, LIGHTNING McQUEEN WILL SPIN OUT!

HERE I AM!

WHAT'S HANGING ON MATER'S HOOK?

WWOOOWWW

PLOF

134

NO TIME TO EXPLAIN, KID! JUST GO OVER THE **SAND** WHEN YOU HIT THE **TURN**, AS I TAUGHT YOU!

OKAY, DOC!

IN ONE SCENE ON THIS PAGE THERE'S AN OBJECT OUT OF PLACE. WHICH ONE IS IT?

WHAT??

SCREEECH

LIGHTNING McQUEEN TAKES THE **CHECKERED** FLAG!

YEAH!

GRRR! I LOST!

...SO I THREW THE BUCKET! SWOOOSH!

HA! HA! GREAT JOB, PAL!

TOO BAD FOR YOU, CHICK-MATER'S GOT **PERFECT AIM!**

The End

CRASH COURSE

FRIENDS AND COLLEAGUES OF MONSTERS, INC., I'M SURE YOU'RE ALL ANXIOUS TO FIND OUT WHO IS THE NEW MONSTER OF THE YEAR!

IT'S ME! I CAN FEEL IT!

MONSTER OF THE YEAR

THE WINNER WILL REPRESENT US AT THE ANNUAL SCARE INDUSTRY SEMINAR.

AND THE WINNER IS ...

RANDALL BOGGS! RANDALL BOGGS!

CUT IT OUT, RANDALL!

137

GASP! NO! NO!

DON'T TELL ME YOU DON'T LIKE THEM! ALL REAL MONSTERS ARE CRAZY ABOUT THEM!

SIGH! I WOULD BE, TOO ... BUT I'M TERRIBLY ALLERGIC TO THEM!

I'M SO ASHAMED OF IT! ONLY MY MOTHER KNOWS!

DON'T WORRY, JUNIOR! WE WON'T TELL ANYONE!

GROAN! LET'S GET BACK TO TRAINING ... ASSUMING IT'LL BE OF ANY USE!

AND SO ...

... A HUNDRED AND TEN ... A HUNDRED AND ELEVEN ...

... TH-TH-THREE!

PANT! I CAN'T GO ON ANY MORE!

THAT'S UNDERSTANDABLE, AFTER A GOOD TEN YARDS OF RUNNING!

...OVER THE NEXT FEW DAYS...

HI! UH... WHAT GRADE ARE YOU IN?

YOU HAVE TO SCARE HIM, EDWIN! NOT MAKE FRIENDS WITH HIM!

AM I ANY SCARIER WITH CONTACT LENSES?

UNTIL...

TERRIBLE NEWS, GUYS!

WATERNOOSE WANTS TO SEE HOW EDWIN'S TRAINING IS GOING!

YIKES! HE'S GOING TO RIP US TO SHREDS... AND I MEAN LITERALLY!

I'LL TRY TO PREPARE HIM! HE'S WAITING FOR US IN THE SCARE ROOM!

THE END

WHO LAUGHS FIRST?

THE END

LET'S COLOR!
IS IT PLAYTIME ALREADY?
LET'S RUN FOR IT!
MISSION ACCOMPLISHED!
COLOR WHEN FINISHED

HAVE FUN PLAYING!

ANSWER ALL THE QUESTIONS, THEN COLOR THE PAGE!

1 BESIDES JUGGLING TIRES, GUIDO'S PLAYING WITH SOMETHING ELSE. CONNECT THE DOTS TO FIND OUT WHAT IT IS.

2 WHICH TWO DETAILS BELOW DON'T BELONG TO GUIDO?

A B C

D E F

146

Answers on page 173

3 ANSWER THESE QUESTIONS CORRECTLY TO COMPLETE THE COLORS OF FILLMORE'S RAINBOW STICKER.

COLOR 1 IS GUIDO JUGGLING THREE TIRES?

YES   NO

COLOR 2 IS FILLMORE A HOT AIR BALLOON?

YES   NO

4 WHICH OF THESE FOUR MOUTHS MATCHES LUIGI'S?

A   B   C   D

147

Answers on page 173

SUNNYSIDE HIDEOUT

Woody wants to get back to Sunnyside to help his friends escape. Can you help him through the maze? Make sure that Woody moves through the maze in a special pattern.

Answer on page 173

Beach postcards

Goofy has printed out four copies of a picture of him taken on the beach, but the printer has modified one detail in three of the pictures. Help him to find the only one that has remained the same as the original.

1

2

3

4

Surprise picnic!

1
2
3
4
5
6
7
8

Donald Duck is an excellent cook. He probably learned from Uncle Scrooge, who used to cook wonderful outdoor lunches. This time, though, the delicious smell has attracted a guest. To discover who he is, put the picture "slices" in the right order.

150

Ice fishing

Donald is fishing in the ice but has caught something unusual. Complete the picture by choosing six correct pieces below. Watch out—some of them don't fit!

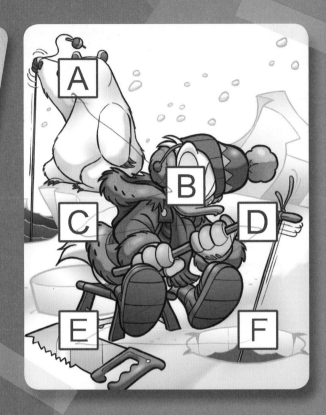

Number game

Mickey Mouse is trying to solve this sudoku puzzle before Goofy sticks his nose in! Help him by adding the missing numbers in the blank squares. The numbers from 1 to 4 cannot be repeated in any column, row, or square.

151

GREAT PUZZLES

Kick back and relax with these fun puzzles!

1 Who is Buzz fighting? Color the areas by using the dots as a color key.

COLOR IN

Answer on page 173

2 Which items resemble these two shadows?

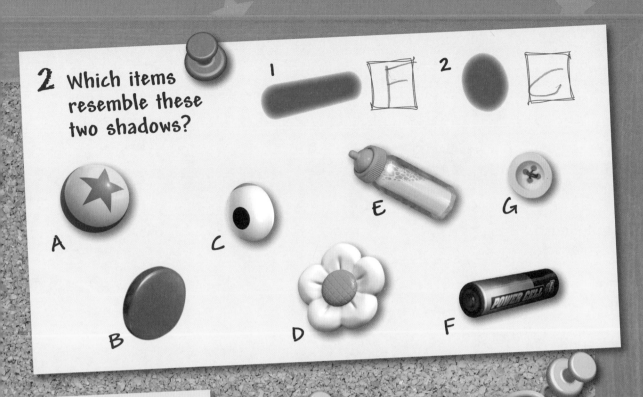

1 ☐ F

2 ☐ G

A
B
C
D
E
G
F

3 Help Lotso find the right line to the heart of his former owner. She has the name of a flower.

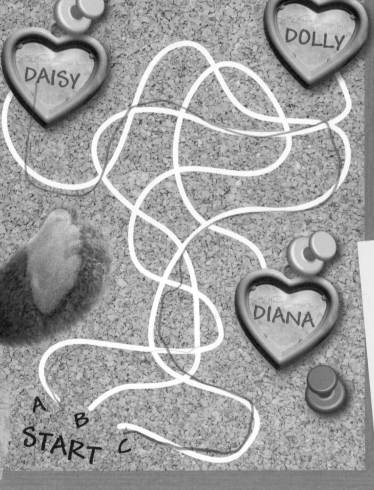

DAISY
DOLLY
DIANA

START
A B C

MISSION ACCOMPLISHED!
COLOR WHEN FINISHED

153

MEDAL QUEST

WHAT YOU NEED:

- 2-4 players
- A die
- A game token for each player (a button or coin)

HOW TO PLAY:

1. Take turns rolling the die to move your game token along the board.
2. Follow the instructions on each square you land on.
3. The first player to land exactly on the Medal of Heroes wins!

MEDAL OF HEROES

FINISH

FELIX FIXES A KART! TAKE AN EXTRA TURN.

6

4

CHEAT CODE MOVE AHEAD 3 SPACES.

2

POWER UP ROLL A 5 TO JUMP TO FIX-IT FELIX, JR. WORLD.

29

POWER UP ROLL A 5 OR JUMP BACK TO GAME CENTRAL STATION.

27

ESCAPE THE FUNGEON MOVE FORWARD 1 SPACE.

SUGAR RUSH WORLD

25

OOPS, A GLITCH! LOSE A TURN.

23

BE THE FIRST TO WIND YOUR WAY THROUGH GAME WORLD TO WIN *WRECK-IT RALPH'S* MEDAL OF HEROES!

7

8

9

FIX-IT FELIX, JR. WORLD

POWER UP
ROLL A 5 TO JUMP TO HERO'S DUTY WORLD.

11

12

START

RALPH WRECKS A WALL
MOVE BACKWARD 2 SPACES.

14

GAME CENTRAL STATION

15

BLAST A CY-BUG!
MOVE FORWARD 1 SPACE.

18

16

CY-BUG AHEAD!
MOVE BACKWARD 1 SPACE.

20

HERO'S DUTY WORLD

POWER UP
ROLL A 5 TO JUMP TO SUGAR RUSH WORLD.

Which destination?

Goofy and Mickey Mouse went camping on their last vacation, but where are they planning to go for their next vacation? To the beach, to the mountains, or to a city? To find out, look at the drawings on the notes. The chosen destination is the one with an odd number of drawings.

City **Beach** **Mountains**

Cheap reflections

Uncle Scrooge has bought such a cheap mirror that it hasn't been able to reflect 13 details. Find them all in less than three minutes!

156

Answers on page 17

Test drive

Donald Duck has had his car adapted and now it's a lot faster! Only one of the shadows perfectly matches the original picture. Which one is it?

1

2

3

4

5

The alarm

Huey, Dewey, and Louie have seen Grandpa Beagle enter Uncle Scrooge's cash stash and have called the police. Who has been able get through to the police? To find out, follow the paths to see which one leads to Grandpa Beagle.

Huey

Dewey

Louie

157

nswers on page 173

1-2-3 PLAY!

PLAY THE GAMES, THEN COLOR THE PAGES!

1

DOC IS WATCHING SOMEONE HOVERING ABOVE THE TRACK. CONNECT THE DOTS FROM 1 TO 24 AND FIND OUT WHO!

2

FIND AND CIRCLE THE PARTS OF THE PICTURE SHOWN BELOW IN THE PICTURE OF HUDSON.

A

B

C

D

E

F

G

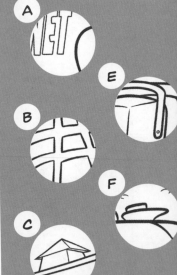

158

Answers on page 173

TEX IS ALSO PROUD OF HIS OPTIONAL HORNS. UNFORTUNATELY, HE'S LOST ONE . . . HELP HIM FIND THE RIGHT ONE FROM AMONG THE THREE BELOW.

3

A

B

C

159

Answer on page 173

PIT STOP

THOSE AREN'T THE RIGHT TIRES, GUIDO! THEY'RE RAIN TIRES!

OH, NO! DO THEY HAVE TO START ARGUING NOW?

THESE HERE ARE MUCH BETTER!

NO! QUESTE!

YOU THINK IT'S GOING TO RAIN? YOU'RE WRONG, MY FRIEND!

HMM . . . MAYBE GUIDO'S RIGHT!

HOW ABOUT A BET, LIGHTNING? IF IT RAINS, I'LL GIVE UP TIRES AND SELL MOTOR OIL!

YOU ALWAYS BLOW EVERYTHING OUT OF PROPORTION, LUIGI! I'LL GO WITH THE RAIN TIRES, GUIDO!

HMPF!

SCREWWW

161

SPACE COMEDY

AND . . . ACTION!

THAT NIGHT, KEN AND CHUNK ARRIVED AT BONNIE'S HOUSE ON A GARBAGE TRUCK . . .

THEY SECRETLY BORROWED THE SUNNYSIDE CAMERA TO SHOOT A MOVIE!

JESSIE WANTS TO GIVE A SPECIAL PRESENT TO BUZZ . . . A SHORT MOVIE FULL OF SPACE ADVENTURES!

JESSIE AND THE ALIENS ARE THE **MAIN CHARACTERS!**

MR. PRICKLEPANTS IS THE **DIRECTOR!**

AND . . . ACTION!

REX IS THE **ALIEN MONSTER!**

UH? G-GROAR!

WHILE KEN TAKES CARE OF THE CAMERA!

AND OF THE COSTUMES!

164

BUT THINGS DON'T GO EXACTLY AS JESSIE HAD PLANNED . . .

JESSIE, SPACE IS IN DANGER! WE NEED THE HELP OF OUR HERO . . .

THE CLAW!

STOP! WHO IS THIS CLAW? IT'S NOT IN THE SCRIPT!

YOU HAVE TO SAY "BUZZ LIGHTYEAR"!

THE CLAW!

SIGH! LET'S MOVE TO THE NEXT SCENE . . .

NEXT SCENE? STOP! CHANGE OF COSTUMES!

167

JIGSAW ROAR

Rex is putting together the pieces of a puzzle of his favorite computer game with Buzz and Zurg. Draw lines to where the pieces belong in the game.

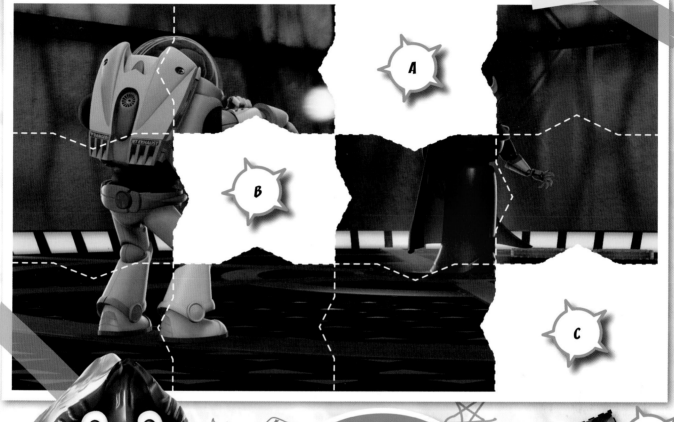

YIKES!
IS BUZZ GOING TO BEAT ZURG?!
THE PRESSURE IS TOO MUCH!

How many dinosaur drawings can you find?

169

TOY PARTS

Trixie, Buttercup, Dolly, and Mr. Pricklepants are trying to figure out which of these items belong to them. Can you help them?

170

A

B

C

D

MISSION ACCOMPLISHED!

COLOUR WHEN FINISHED.

Answers on page 173

ANSWERS

PAGE 7

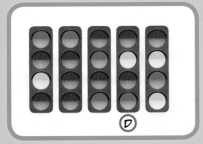

PAGE 17

PAGES 18–19

1

2

BLUE
P T C
8 + 7 + 7 = 22

YELLOW
I O U
5 + 8 + 9 = 22

RED
S N P
8 + 12 + 8 = 28

PAGE 20

NAME DROPPING
Wazowski

ALL FOR ONE
Shadow B

PAGE 21

PAGE 24

REX, BUZZ, BARBIE, KEN, WOODY,
JESSIE, SLINKY, LOTSO

PAGES 26–27

SOCCER
TWINS?

LUCKY
KICK

THE BIG MATCH
B

PAGE 29

PAGE 31

1: Phineas and Ferb's house, 2: Doofenshmirtz
Evil Incorporated, 3: Agent P's secret lair, 4:
Phineas and Ferb's backyard, 5: Candace's
room, 6: Dr. Doofenshmirtz's lab, 7: OWCA
Headquarters, 8: Ferb's side of the bedroom,
9: Mr. Slushy Burger, 10: Googolplex Mall

PAGES 32–33

HIDE-AND-SEEK
Mike Wazowski

DID YOU SEE THAT?

PAGE 47

A: ROR, B: OK, C: ROR,
D: OK, E: EEK, F: JOX

PAGE 49

OUT OF FOCUS
C

FIND THE DETAILS
A: 5, B: 3, C: 2, D: 1, E: 4

PAGES 50–51

SOCCER FIX
A: 1, B: 4, C: 5

A GAME OF SHADOWS
B

A REFLECTION OF GOLD

ORIGINAL T-SHIRT
14

PAGES 52–53

1 1: C, 2: A, 3: B
2 1: A, 2: C, 3: B
3 A, C, D
4 Seven stars

PAGES 56-57

1 POLE POSITION
A: 6, B: 8, C: 2, D: 7, E: 3, F: 1, G: 5, H: 4

2 INTERNATIONAL FLAGS

3 ADD UP THE TIRES
Francesco: 2 + 2 + 1 +1 = 6 laps
Nigel: 1 + 1 + 1 + 1 = 4 laps
Jeff: 3 + 3 + 2 + 2 = 10 laps
Raoul: 3 + 3 + 1 + 1 = 8 laps
Jeff will make the most laps.

PAGES 60-61

FIX THE WALL, FELIX!
1: C, 2: I, 3: E, 4: G, 5: F, 6: A

FIND THE CY-BUG!
C

A MESS OF CANDY!

PAGES 62-63

1: Doofenshmirtz House in the Suburbs
2: Doofenshmirtz Evil is Carpeted
3: Doofenshmirtz Wicked Witch Castle
4: Doofenshmirtz Abandoned Vacuum Cleaner Factory
5: Doofenshmirtz Carbon Footprint
6: Doofenshmirtz Hideout-shaped Island

PAGE 64

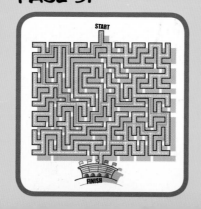

PAGE 65

PUZZLE STORIES
A: 3, B: 4, C: 1

PASSES

PAGES 82-83

PAGES 84-85

THE BEST SOLUTION IS:

PAGE 90

UNUSUAL PENALTY
Left to right: D, B, C, E, A

SUPER DRIBBLING

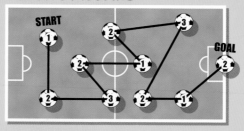

PAGE 91

PAGES 92-93

WORD WRECK
A: Sugar, B: Candy, C: Wreck,
D: Niceland, E: Racer, F: Level,
G: Hammer, H: Hero, I: Soldier

EXTREME CLOSE-UP
A: A Cy-bug, B: A gun,
C: Ralph's hand, D: Calhoun's hair,
E: Calhoun's mouth, F: Ralph's foot

PAGES 94-95

COLOR MASH-UP
Mr. Potato Head's ear, Mrs. Potato Head's hand, Jessie's hair, Bullseye's ear, Buzz's toe

THE RIGHT HAT
Jessie: F
Woody: E

PAGE 116

WHERE'S THE SCHOOL OF SCARING?

PAGE 117

CHET'S SHADOW
B

MONSTER SUDOKU

PAGE 123

There are 11 Rs

PAGES 124–125

SNACK TIME!

BAG LIFTING

MONEY MAKER

REFRESHING DESSERT
There are 33 lollies

PAGES 126–127

MISSING PIECES
A: 5, B: 4, C: 3, D: 1, E: 6, F: 2

FANS' LOOKS
1: C, 2: D, 3: A, 4: B

A FAN'S FLAGS
C

PAGE 128

COLORS OF THE RING

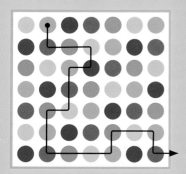

MONSTERS GROW UP!
A: 2, B: 3, C: 1

PAGE 132
3

PAGE 133
D

PAGES 146–147

1
A nut

2
D and F

3
Color 1: Yes, Color 2: No

4
D

PAGES 148–149

SUNNYSIDE HIDEOUT

PAGE 150

BEACH POSTCARDS
2

SURPRISE PICNIC!
Top to bottom: 6, 8, 2, 5, 7, 4, 1, 3

PAGE 151

ICE FISHING
A: 8, B: 4, C: 11, D: 2, E: 5, F: 7

NUMBER GAME

2	3	1	4
4	1	3	2
1	2	4	3
3	4	2	1

PAGES 152–153

1
Zurg

2
1: F, 2: C

3
C: Daisy

PAGES 156–157

WHICH DESTINATION?
Mountains

CHEAP REFLECTIONS

TEST DRIVE
5

THE ALARM
Dewey

PAGES 158–159

1 Dinoco Helicopter

2

3
C

PAGE 169
A: 3, B: 1, C: 2
There are five dinosaur drawings!

PAGE 170

Trixie: C, Buttercup: D, Dolly: A,
Mr. Pricklepants: B